DEDICATION

*To everyone who has ADHD and the people
who care about them. Which pretty much includes
everyone, whether they realize it or not.*

ADD
Stole My
Car Keys

The surprising ways
Adult Attention Deficit Hyperactivity Disorder affects your life…
and strategies for creating a life you love.

Rick Green & Umesh Jain, M.D., PH.D.

ADD STOLE MY CAR KEYS

The surprising ways Adult Attention Deficit Hyperactivity Disorder affects your life…
and strategies for creating a life you love.

© 2011 Big Brain Productions Inc. and Jainsco Inc.

First edition

Published by Big Brain Productions

PO Box 39554
RPO Lakeshore Cawthra
Mississauga, ON

L5G 4S6

Cover and Interior Design: Carmelo Galati, *www.SeesawCreative.ca*

Illustrated by Bryce Hallett, *www.FrogFeetProductions.com*

Publishers Cataloging-in-Publication

Green, Rick & Jain, Umesh.
ADD Stole My Car Keys. The surprising ways Adult Attention Deficit Hyperactivity Disorder affects your life and strategies for creating a life you love / Rick Green & Umesh Jain- 1st ed.

p.cm

Includes medical & scientific references & sources and index

ISBN 978-0-9866240-2-5

1. Attention-deficit disorder in adults-Popular works 2. Attention-deficit disorder in adults-Strengths. 3. Attention-deficit disorder in adults symptoms. 4. Attention-deficit disorder in adults-Strategies.

1. Title

Table of Contents

Chapter One: Common Beliefs ADHD People Share

Chapter Two: Signs From Childhood

Chapter Three: Common Behaviours in ADDers

Chapter Four: Common Misbehaviours

Chapter Five: Signs of Inattention in Adults

Chapter Six: Signs of Hyperactivity and Impulsivity

Chapter Seven: Disorders That Resemble, or Combine with ADHD

Chapter Eight: Familiar Frustrations of ADHD Adults

Chapter Nine: Familiar Complaints of the ADDer's Family

Chapter Ten: Ways ADHD Impacts Work and Finances

Chapter Eleven: Ways of Unconsciously Coping

Chapter Twelve: Amazing, Unexpected, Sometimes Hidden, Often Unappreciated Strengths of ADHD Adults

Acknowledgements

We would like to thank our wives, Ava Green and Preeti Jain, for their love, patience and encouragement. We want to thank our children to whom we hope we leave a better world. Dr. J would like to thank his new puppy, who reminds him that even animals can have ADHD and love life.

A special thanks to Patrick & Janis McKenna, whose courage in sharing their path to discovery has helped more people than they will ever know. We are all indebted to them for the documentary, *ADD & Loving It?!* and all that it has inspired. We are also indebted to Michael Kot, Lynne Carter and Canwest Global Television for trusting a comedian to create *ADD & Loving It?!*

Thanks as well to Jimi Doidge for showing up at the office every day and making work so much fun. To Aerin & Jimmy Guy, Jennifer Johnson, Pam Sinclair & Bruce Doidge, The Secret Location and everyone else who has worked on, or contributed to, the TotallyADD. com website.

To Dr. Edward Hallowell, Dr. Laura Muggli, Dr. Steven Kurtz, Dr. Lenard Adler, Dr. Margaret Weiss, Dr. Annick Vincent, Kate Kelly and Thom Hartmann for sharing what they have learned.

Thanks Gina Pera for her enthusiasm. Ruth Hughes and everyone at CHADD for their endorsement and ongoing collaboration. Thanks to ADDA for letting so many people know about us. Heidi Bernhardt at CADDAC for her tireless dedication to the cause. Alan Foster and the good folks at EPS for getting us on PBS, and the amazing, dedicated people at PBS who made sure the word got out to millions of families.

Thanks to Mike Mancuso and Ava Green for editing our words so they actually made sense. To Carm Galati and Bryce Hallett, we are inspired by your creativity and grateful to work with such classy, funny guys.

And thanks to you for having the courage to buy this book and take on your life with a growing sense of what is possible.

Preface

We want to make you smile. Life is full of challenges and the life of the ADDer has extra hurdles. Humor is your best defense. Both as a shield and a sword. When you can laugh at something, it diminishes the fear.

The book is built around 155 ADDer's personal experiences. These capture the range of beliefs, challenges and symptoms that adults with ADHD commonly struggle. Dr. Jain, a psychiatrist specializing in ADHD, reveals the facts. Rick Green, a comedian who has ADHD, shares his best and worst moments. Feel free to laugh.

We use this simple structure because ADDers can be impatient; they prefer to-the-point commentary. This book was designed to deliver what you need to know in easily digestible bites. Besides we have trouble focusing long enough to write ponderous Chapters.

Not every one of the 155 'signs' will apply to you. The human brain is complex. Each person's situation is different, so every ADDer is unique. Yet they have much in common.

If you have been diagnosed with ADHD, this may feel like your personal log. We have written it so that you can recognize your own story. Some of this is our opinion, based upon our experiences. We hope that it resonates with you. Feel free to write all over the book, "Yes!" "No!" "That's my Dad!"

If you have never been diagnosed but suspect you might have ADHD, you may recognize yourself in these pages, again and again. You may experience a growing sense of familiarity, or a lightning bolt of insight, a feeling of having arrived, or even feeling stark naked and totally exposed. Rather chilling isn't it?! The good news is, now you know. Now you have a chance of getting a handle on it. (But first, get some clothes on! You're naked for God's sake!)

Of course, you will want more information. You can begin your journey of discovery at www.TotallyADD.com. We have created this community to provide useful Tools and Strategies, and point you to other books and online resources.

So laugh and chuckle, but trust that this book contains reliable information about ADHD. We have written it as a primer, so that after you stop chuckling or squirming or crying your eyes out over all the needless suffering you've been through, you will be armed with a clear sense of what ADHD is, and what it is not.

Introduction

Attention Deficit Hyperactivity Disorder (ADHD) is the most common developmental neuropsychiatric disorder of childhood, and by default, one of the most common disorders in adulthood. This is a chronic, highly heritable, neurological condition. And undiagnosed, it sucks.

If you're new to Adult ADHD, prepare to be surprised. Much or all of what you know may be wrong. Scientific breakthroughs in genetics and new brain imaging technologies are shedding new light on the neurology. But the mythology lives on and on and on…

Let's start with the name. While the lay public will often use the terms ADD and ADHD interchangeably, they are different.

ADD individuals have problems with Inattention. (Like focusing, distractibility, sticking to things.) Whereas ADHD folks also have two more challenges: Impulsivity and Motor Hyperactivity (which may evolve by adulthood into internalized anxiety and/or restlessness.) So everyone, whether ADD or ADHD, has the Inattentive symptoms. ADHD folks also have Hyperactivity and Impulsivity. We explore these three areas in detail.

In this book, we sometimes use ADD to cover both ADD and ADHD, if what we're talking about applies to both.

The diagnosis is defined by the Diagnostic and Statistical Manual (DSM) by the American Psychiatric Association. This book is the standard reference for doctors. It is constantly being revised and the Fifth Edition is expected in 2013. Or 2014. Or 2015. (ADDers aren't the only ones with issues around deadlines.)

We explore many associated symptoms, such as procrastination and organizational problems, which are not part of the diagnostic criteria but will certainly resonate with ADHD adults.

There are many 'tests' and 'questionnaires' around; some are quite good. The Adult ADHD Self Report Scale (ASRS), for example, is on our website, www.TotallyADD.com. We haven't included any quizzes in this book because none of them are diagnostic. But they can certainly act as a screener tool. In other words they cannot provide a definitive Yes or No, but they can suggest, "Boy this is looking more likely." Or "Hmm, maybe something else is going on with me."

If you're struggling, seek an assessment by a professional. There is a great deal that can be done to turn things around. A holistic approach, involving the mind and the body, can be transformative. That is the good news and it's the place to focus your attention. Especially if you have trouble focusing!

Chapter One

Common Beliefs ADHD People Share

Even in childhood you knew you were different. But you couldn't explain how or why.

You may not know why life is so challenging, why you can't focus, have trouble finishing things, or get bored so easily. You may be a daydreamer, restless, and/or impulsive… and you struggle. Even over simple things. Until you get a reliable diagnosis of ADHD you will create other explanations for 'what is wrong with me'. By adulthood you may have developed strong beliefs about yourself and the world. Mostly negative ones. The few positives you do see are always qualified, "I'm creative, but I never manage to…" Or, "I have a good heart, but I can't seem to…" A belief is not the truth.

But it can become your 'truth.' It will take courage to consider that what you 'know for sure' may actually be a judgment, based on misinterpretation, skewed perceptions and incomplete information. As an adult with ADHD (sometimes called ADD) you have probably built up a lifetime of beliefs that don't serve you. They will certainly limit you in ways you never fully appreciated. Taking apart beliefs is intimidating… and exhilarating. Let's explore some common perceptions and misperceptions that ADDers have about themselves. In the process we'll uncover the history of ADHD and see how our understanding has evolved over the past fifty years.

1.

Massive Denial

"ADHD? I don't have a mental disorder. I don't rant or rave or have delusions. My brain is fine. Sure, I make mistakes but everyone does. I am unique, but I am NOT abnormal."

If my doctor tells me, "This ultrasound shows that your gall bladder has a problem," I assume it's true. Yet if my doctor suggests my brain has a problem, I want to shout, "Not me!" Why the denial? I think it's because ADHD is not an illness we catch. The ADHD brain is hardwired this way. It's our normal. We have never experienced anything else, so we can't compare. No wonder we prefer to believe, "This is just how I am."

If there isn't a blood test or ultrasound to identify ADHD then how can my doctor be sure? Dr. J?

ADHD is tricky to spot. Because everyone has problems with focusing or restlessness now and then. Something is called a mental 'disorder' if there are enough impairing symptoms; a threshold beyond which we know statistically can't happen by chance. The symptoms for ADHD, and every other disorder, are listed in the Diagnostic and Statistical Manual, 4th Edition-Text Revision (DSM-IV-TR) produced by the American Psychiatric Association (1). ADHD is one of the most treatable mental health conditions around so it is very important to make an accurate diagnosis. Time to take action!

2.

Wilting Power

"Everyone says if I would just try harder and stick with it, I'd be great. And they're right. But I do try and I can't stick with it. I'm a quitter. No will power."

 If someone with Parkinson's disease suppressed their tremors for a few seconds, would you tell them, "See, you just need to try harder." Ridiculous, right? Just because someone can temporarily stop a behavior does not mean its voluntary.

The ADDer can complete a task in one situation but not in another, so outsiders conclude that they aren't trying hard enough. But, ADHD is not a will power disorder. The ADDer may feel a kind of paralysis; like something is switched off. We call this a 'negative symptom' because the circuit is disconnected; it's not working effectively. The ADDer laments, "I know what to do, but I just can't make myself do it." This feeling of helplessness is frustrating. We'll explore the neurobiology behind this in the later chapters. But be clear, it is neurobiology. Not morality. Not laziness.

 I was in awe of friends who could spend six hours straight and complete their taxes. Magical! Meanwhile, I could spend hours, days, even weeks mastering the sleight of hand for a magic trick. Clearly I had will power. But it was selective. After taking on my ADHD, I can do both, master a magic trick and also get my taxes in… Okay, I'm late this year, but usually, I mean, mostly… Okay, once. Ahem.

3.

Seemingly *Self Sabotaging*

"I can't be trusted. But I desperately want people to trust me. I do incredibly well for a while then, BAM, completely blow it. Do I fear success? Why do I seem to sabotage my finances and relationships? What's wrong with me? I'm such a stupid loser!"

A poem titled 'Fidgety Phil' perfectly captures the symptoms of ADHD (2). It was written in 1844! Clearly this is not a recent phenomenon. By about 1900 doctors started calling those same symptoms, 'A Defect of Moral Control' (3). In the 1950's it was renamed 'Minimal Brain Dysfunction' (4). It wasn't until 1975 that ADHD was clearly defined. Even then it was only regarded as a childhood disorder (5).

No one realized it continued into adulthood until 1989 (6). We now know that about 1 in 25 adults have the disorder (7). So where was Adult ADHD hiding before 1989? Well, it was misdiagnosed, probably as anxiety and/or depression. It's not hard to see why. Imagine a child constantly barraged with negative comments. Eventually the correcting and scolding becomes an internal belief, "I'm not good enough". They become their own worst enemy, creating the basis for a mood and anxiety disorder. But the fact is, Adult ADHD has always been with us.

I know so many ADDers, including yours truly, who mistook their ADHD for Depression. After a while, it IS depressing!

4.

Dare to Daydream

"I wasn't bouncing off the classroom walls. Quite the opposite. I was quiet, never a problem for the teacher. The reason I barely passed was that I was lost in thought. Spaced out. Forgetful. The teachers all agreed I had potential, but as my Irish mom said, 'You were always off with the fairies.'"

The standard doctor's diagnostic manual, the DSM-IV-TR, lists 9 symptoms, or signs, of Inattention. Very few people have them all. But one only has to meet the threshold of at least 6 of the 9 symptoms to have a diagnosis of ADHD (8). The person quoted above would be called the Predominantly Inattentive Subtype. This is the non-hyperactive version of ADHD. In lay terms, we call this Attention Deficit Disorder or ADD. These people tend to be quiet introverts. It's more common in girls; no one knows why. Because these kids aren't hyperactive or impulsive and driving their teacher into early retirement, they often slide under the radar.

Oh yes, there are Subtypes of ADHD! Dr. J warned you that this is tricky to figure out. So ADDers fall into two main subtypes: those with problems of Inattention, and those who ALSO have problems with Hyperactivity and Impulsivity. Confused? Good. Read on!

5.

Close But *No Cigar*

"I read a list of ADHD symptoms and sure, some rang a bell, but who isn't forgetful and a bit jumpy nowadays? I was boisterous as a kid, but every class has a troublemaker. Plus, there are a bunch of the symptoms that didn't apply to me at all. Sorry, no sale."

 If someone has problems with Inattention then we ask, what about Hyperactivity and Impulsivity? The standard reference book, the DSM-IV-TR, lists 9 symptoms of Hyperactivity/ Impulsivity. If the person has 6 or more symptoms, they may have the Predominantly Combined Subtype. This is the most common type of ADHD.

If an adult doesn't quite meet the threshold of at least 6 of 9, but the symptoms they do have are wrecking their life, they might be referred to as ADHD, Not Otherwise Specified (NOS). Many experts argue that adults with ADHD should actually have a lower threshold than 6 out of 9 since any of the symptoms can be painfully impairing (9).

 By age 40 I had found ways to manage my undiagnosed ADHD. Mostly I avoided stuff where I struggled. After learning about ADHD, I could see that my coping strategies were really hit and miss. No wonder. Hard to hit a target you can't see and don't know is there. Recognizing my specific impairments and then targeting them has been way more efficient.

6.

Cross Cultural *Curse*

"I'm Jamaican and we are very expressive people. We are not all ADHD. You can't condemn an entire culture."

ADHD is everywhere; in every culture, country and ethnic group. It's genetic, not cultural or racial. Seventy six percent of a person's ADHD comes from their genes (10). I always ask the ADDer, "Who in the family reminds you of you?" It is so strongly genetic that if a person doesn't have any relatives with similar issues, I question the diagnosis.

In fact, the number one reason adults seek help is because their child is diagnosed and they recognize the same traits in themselves. Suddenly their past starts making sense. This is the beginning of their emotional journey.

Journey? You mean roller coaster ride! When my son was tested in Grade 7, I demanded to see the quizzes. As a responsible parent, that I am on occasion, I read each test carefully. Eventually I realized I have more of these symptoms than my son!

Just my luck, I finally score high on some tests, and they explain why I never scored high on tests!

7.

Poof, It's Gone!

"Yes, I was diagnosed with ADHD in Grade 7. I was even on medication. I forget which one. But our doctor assured my mom this was a childhood thing. And I pretty well grew out of it."

Back in 1957 Dr. Lafleur wrote a paper that suggested ADHD is a childhood disorder that burns out by adolescence (11). What no one understood back then was that ADHD symptoms change through adolescence so it looks like the disorder disappears. A Long Term Outcome study published in 1989 by Drs. Weiss and Hechtman from McGill University (12) clearly showed that ADHD is a chronic, lifespan disorder. The study has since been replicated (13, 14) validating their initial findings. We now know that about 60% of ADHD children continue to have impairing symptoms into adulthood (15).

By adulthood I could control my restlessness and sit through a meeting, apparently listening. But mentally, I'd be imagining a SWAT Team crashing through the windows, guns blazing... Or whatever. Once I had a proper diagnosis, I managed my restlessness with far less effort.

ADDers such as billionaire Richard Branson, Olympic Medalist Michael Phelps, and TV host Ty Pennington did not succeed by changing who they are, but by figuring out how to minimize their struggles and maximize what they love doing. Even I have learned how to focus and be present during meetings. (But if a SWAT Team attacks, I'm ready.)

8.

Selective *Stupidity* Syndrome

"How can someone in my position have done so many stupid things? I have been reasonably successful at work but with my home life and finances… I keep blowing it! Again. And Again. Why?!"

The internalization of negative comments (that "I'm not good enough" voice) is called a Cognitive Distortion. Essentially, we think bad, we feel bad. Fortunately, this negative thinking can be challenged and corrected. For example, I could have confronted the person quoted above with, "Do you have an IQ less than 40? No? Then you are not an idiot. OK you made a few mistakes, but you have gained valuable experience. And look at all your successes. Don't diminish or dismiss them." It is crucial for ADDers to learn how to stop these negative cognitions.

I was my own worst enemy. A Drama King. My mood tanked every time I screwed up. Then I'd have to rally myself to recover. And if someone else pointed out a mistake, I was totally defensive. Because what I believed was, "I am a screw up." When I understood ADHD was not a character flaw, I could challenge my internal voice. Now when things get difficult, I remind myself, "It's okay. Relax… I'm fine. I'm good. I'm great. I'm a GOD!!! An All Powerful GOD!!!" (Okay, I may be overcompensating.)

9.

The *Whole World* is Frustrating!

"I find so many things frustrating! I don't understand. Is it just me? Are there unspoken rules that everyone else seems to know? Why won't someone tell me what they are?"

Sometimes the ADHD adult feels like modern life is a game and they are the only one who doesn't know the rules. So when they fail they're baffled and wonder what went wrong? Eventually they can develop a belief that life is unfair and unjust. They question basic societal processes like: Work first, then have fun! Why? Finish school then there will be success. Why? Pay your dues. Why? Work your way to the top. Why?

An ADDer may think they should be made the CEO of the company immediately and not have to follow the traditional path to success. Alas, that's not how the world works.

I want to know who made up all these rules? Certainly not us ADDers. Modern life requires us to fit in. There are due dates, appointment times and submission deadlines. We are told, "That's how it's done." Ironically, without us ADDers, that is probably how things would always be done. When we master our impairing symptoms we can be the most creative people around. When you develop control over the "Hyperactive, Impulsive and Inattentive" symptoms they become "Energetic, Spontaneous and Imaginative". Yee hiiii!

10.

Is *Underachiever-osis* a Disease?

"By God, I have potential. I know it. Every teacher said so. I can sense it! I just can't ever seem to achieve it. Why do I eventually disappoint everyone, including myself?"

ADDers often sense they have real strengths but they may not develop them because they are busy handling all the screw-ups resulting from their ADHD. Life becomes crisis management, 24/7. Totally reactive. They may even grow used to it. Chaos becomes 'the norm'. No wonder so many of my adult clients are frustrated knowing they have the potential to achieve great things, if only they could push past all the petty background noise of life.

Oh, man. That was my life. Overwhelming problems. Never achieving what I felt I could. Like, I was in a batting cage and someone kept speeding up the pitches. Everyday life seemed to emphasize my weaknesses. All I could see were my failures and what I had done wrong; there was no sense of accomplishment, despite, for example, having written and performed 500 episodes of television. Undiagnosed ADHD is a recipe for exhaustion and depression. People fear this diagnosis, but I say, "Knowing can save your life. And give you access to achieve what you want."

11.

A Rebel *Without* Applause

"I'm weird. I don't think like everyone else. I see things others miss and yet miss stuff they all seem to see. I just don't fit anywhere. I didn't fit into my classroom, I don't fit into my family, I don't fit at my job. And to be honest, part of me doesn't want to fit in."

 I sometimes felt like I was born into the wrong universe; an 8-Track player in a Blu-ray world. This sense of being different left me feeling sad and lonely. Convinced I was weird, unreliable, and weak-willed, I tried to work around my weaknesses, but never noticed how much the impairments were costing me. Now I can see how shut down I was. Scary.

 ADDers are often the black sheep of the family; the scapegoat for everyone's problems. If they choose to minimize their impairments and relish in their differences then they might become successful. That's why it's crucial to know they have it. As many of my clients tell me, "Just getting the diagnosis was 50% of the battle. What a relief! My life suddenly made sense!"

 The square peg learns how to become rounded when they need to, and how to make their world more square.

12.

The Mirror's *Broken*

"People are shallow, short-sighted, dunderheads. What are they thinking? Can't they see what's important? Can't they see what I see? I'm fine! It's everyone else! How come no one appreciates my point of view?"

Many ADDers are lousy at self-assessment. They may not appreciate the errors of their ways because they might have difficulty seeing anyone else's point of view. Unable to monitor and self-reflect, they make the same mistakes over and over again. Therapy can help. Therapy is like a mirror, giving them a reflection of what others see.

For example, someone suggests the ADDer talks too loud. If they don't respect that person's opinion, the ADDer dismisses the complaint. If they do trust the person, and are shown how to turn down the volume, the ADDer wants to take it on. The secret is to seek feedback from trusted sources.

We are not very good at self-observation. But we think we are. Which proves how bad we are at self-observation. I didn't appreciate how much I dominated conversations until someone videotaped me. Try it; ask someone to videotape you. Yes, it can be mortifying, but better you should know. Watch yourself on tape and let go of thoughts such as, "Do I really sound like that?" Or in my case, "Wow, am I really that good looking?"

 Which proves how bad he is at self-observation.

 Who? Me?

Chapter Two

Signs From Childhood

Every adult with ADHD was once a child with ADHD.

According to the doctor's standard reference, the DSM-IV-TR, the symptoms of ADHD are there in childhood. If you only had Inattentive symptoms you may have slid under the radar; the shy daydreamer isn't disruptive. Whereas ADHD was painfully obvious if you were also Hyperactive and Impulsive.

Can you remember what you were like at age seven? Probably not. ADDers have poor memory skills; you may not even remember much about yesterday. Therefore it can be incredibly enlightening to ask a parent, older sibling or a relative for their memories of you. If you were a handful, they will have stories! You may be sick of hearing them, but your loved ones never tire of telling them.

Elementary school report cards, or tests you have taken, may also offer clues to your youth. Even old home movies can be revealing, "Wow, I never stop moving!"

You may have learned to hide some of your symptoms, but people could tell you were different. At the time, they said you were a handful, a daydreamer or a chatterbox.

Understanding the symptoms of ADHD may suddenly clarify your whole life story. Connections appear, quirks are explained, and failures make sense. Inside this new context your story starts to piece itself together in a way that finally 'feels right.'

13.

Michael the *Menace*

"As a kid I was a whirling dervish. Oh, the stories my mom tells. Now, I watch our spirited two year old and think, 'Uh oh.' And my mom just smiles at me, with a look that says, 'Payback!'"

 I've found that many ADHD kids display a kind of ambivalence; conflicting energies, if you will. They seem frightened of the world, yet, hell bent on twisting it to their agenda. There is an unspoken message to their parents, especially Mom, "Don't try to control me! I'll do whatever I want! But I don't trust the world. So stay where I can see you, in case things go badly and I need help."

Mom complains, "It's like the terrible two's never stopped." It's no wonder there are higher rates of maternal depression and divorce in these families (16).

 ADHD kids can be a natural contraceptive; once you have one, who wants another? The Depression and World War 2 were good training for my parents to handle my brother and I. And hey, they gave us our genes!

14.

"If only…" Report Cards

"All of my report cards said, "A very bright student who could do much better if only he could focus on his own work instead of talking, arguing, and interrupting others." The basic theme was always, 'He has so much potential, if only…'"

The core ADHD symptom of Inattention disrupts a child's academic performance. But it is the symptoms of Impulsiveness and Motor Restlessness that drive teachers crazy. ADHD kids push buttons relentlessly. A teacher who can handle an ADHD child, frankly, can handle any child. Parents will often tell me that if, at the start of the school year, the new teacher understands ADHD, their child will be OK this year. Otherwise the best they can expect is, "Good news Mom, only three detentions this week."

All of my report cards featured a bunch of C's, a B minus in Art and a D in Phys Ed. Always with the same teacher's comment: "Ricky is underachieving and could do much better if he would pay attention more and not daydream." Yeah, and my friend who had Polio could do better at sports if he stopped walking funny. The one thing I do know is that the girl in my class who got straight A's didn't have many friends either. Now I'm married to a straight A's girl. Who's the dummy now, Mrs. Femssen?!

15.

Lost in *La-La Land*

"At school I got an 'A' in daydreaming. And I was always disorganized. I would forget assignments or lose things. My salvation from total boredom was the science fiction novels I inhaled while pretending to read Wuthering Heights. I couldn't wait to graduate. In fact, I didn't."

Inattention directly impacts school grades. The scattered brain, (lost in space, struggling with time perception and poor organization) leads to immense impairment. This eventually disrupts the whole learning experience. ADHD kids soon become cynical, disinterested and isolated. Traditional school doesn't engage them. Things are, however, slowly changing. Parents must continue to advocate to make the school system equitable. These kids are precious.

I'd be in the middle of combat, blasting a bunch of Nazis who were attacking my platoon, when, BAM! My teacher's nasal voice snapped me back to reality, "Ricky, what do you think the denominator is?" Caught, I'd blurt out, "The Treaty of Versailles?" Mrs. Femssen had noticed I was zoned out, but rather than catch my eye and bring me back to the lesson, she embarrassed me in front of my giggling peers. She is long gone, and thankfully so is the belief that public humiliation motivates kids.

16.

Act Your Age

"When I was a kid I didn't have a lot of friends, but the ones I did have were either two or three years younger than me, or much older. And I was always the follower."

It's "The 30% Rule" (17). Knock 30% off of an ADD child's age and that is their level of maturity. A 15 year-old acts like an 11-year-old. A 10 year-old behaves like he is 7. As well, adolescence just seems to last longer. They really don't seem to mature as fast. Of course, when they come into midlife, people will admire their "youthful vitality". Until then, the maturity gap comes with considerable baggage. "Don't be such a goof!"

Most of my classmates couldn't wait to grow up. Not me. In public school my friends were all two grades back. In university, my best friends were still in high school. Until I was diagnosed, in mid-life, I had this sense of 'avoiding adulthood activities.' Responsibility seemed like a bad thing. It meant being blamed or being at fault; rather than being in charge and in control. Even now I can be juvenile, which I mistake for being youthful. Until my wife explains the difference. Ahem.

17.

Mediocre Mensa

"A number of years ago I did an IQ test in a magazine and scored 'genius'. What a relief! Secretly, I always felt smart, but I didn't have much evidence. I always did so poorly in school that I felt like a dummy."

Really smart children need high levels of stimulation to function, just like ADHD kids. However, there is a popular Internet-based statistic people may have heard, which is that 50% of gifted children fall into the ADHD spectrum. So far this is not backed up by any formal study, but the implications are nonetheless real. ADHD and Giftedness are significantly different. Either one creates problems for the school system. Put them together… well, no wonder there is an explosion of alternative schools.

Being fairly smart didn't help much with my schoolwork or grades. It just allowed me to invent more creative excuses when I screwed up. Since I didn't know what the real issue was, I thought up some very clever explanations about what was wrong with me. Add a dose of puberty, thick glasses and corduroy pants and no wonder my adolescence was hell.

18.

Darwinian *Blunder*

"I was never the one who started the trouble! But I'd be the one who was caught. I'd overreact to some teasing or bullying and start throwing punches. Ok, sometimes I did start it, but it was a joke. Can't people take a joke?"

I've worked with many ADD kids who got into trouble because they overreacted to a conflict. Other kids knew that they had poor self-control, so they exploited it, teasing and goading. As well, the ADHD kid's impulsivity, poor judgment and their need to be accepted by anyone makes them an easy target. They get caught, even when someone else instigates it. The fall guy. This story, unfortunately, gets repeated into adulthood. 40% of the prison population has undiagnosed ADHD (18).

No wonder the jails are full of ADDers. We're so impatient, clumsy, disorganized and prone to mistakes; we can't even do crime right! Criminal mastermind? I don't think so.

19.

Birthday *Crash*

"I wasn't invited to a lot of birthday parties or sleepovers. I didn't make friends easily. I wasn't trying to be a pain, but I didn't know how to stop myself... no self control."

ADHD individuals have difficulty interpreting social cues. For example, they cannot distinguish what is genuinely humorous from what is annoyingly silly. Other kids may laugh but no one wants to be friends with 'the goof.' When they take on treatment and improve, kids usually tell me, "My parents don't yell as much, school is more interesting and people like me more." Having friends is an important protective factor. Treating the ADHD improves a child's self-esteem (19).

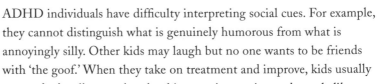

When someone claims ADHD is just about lazy teachers or indulgent parents, "And these kids should be left to enjoy being kids with their friends," I want to scream, "They have no friends. They don't enjoy being like this!" Ask any Adult ADDer about their childhood. It's never pretty.

Sure we want our kids to get good grades, but what matters most is that they have friends and are invited to birthday parties. Self-esteem comes from actual accomplishments! And without help these kids fail! Their suffering is avoidable!!... Sorry, I'll get down off my soapbox now.

20.

"The Lady doth protest *too much*"

"My parents resisted my ADHD diagnosis. Especially my Dad. He thought I was perfectly normal... a chip off the old block. He argued that my teachers were just control freaks who wanted kids to be goody-goody-two-shoes."

Behind a parent's anger is fear. Fear of what this diagnosis implies. Parents feel responsible and worry their child is damaged perhaps doomed. The emotionality spirals. I've found that if Mom or Dad is fanatically opposed to the possibility of ADHD, it's because their child reminds them of themselves at that age and that intensifies their helplessness. The opposite is also true. If the parents don't seem upset at all, it may be because they also have undiagnosed ADHD and they don't see the problem.

At first I was scared to get diagnosed, "What if my brain isn't normal?" Then I'd watch some reality TV and think, "Define normal." My brain is simply inefficient at certain tasks and terrific at others. As for people who adamantly denounce my diagnosis? It reminds me of those televangelists and politicians who righteously rave against the sin of homosexuality... until they're caught in a men's room with their personal trainer, Bruno.

21.

High School *Hell*

"I dropped out of high school. I couldn't hack it. My marks were always crappy, so it wasn't any great loss. I figured, 'What am I learning this for? I'm never going to use this stuff.' And I haven't."

 School is challenging for everyone. For an ADHD child it's particularly stressful during Grade SK/1, Grade 4, Grade 7/8 and the entry into University. Why those times? In Grade 4 school typically moves from learning skills to applying them, "Now you can print, write a story." During Grade 7/8 there is an emphasis on self-directed abilities, like homework. At University/College there is no accountability, so without internal fortitude, ADDers flounder. Brute intelligence may see them through, often aided by self-medicating with caffeine, energy drinks and nicotine.

 I remember High School. (Shudder!) One teacher, Mr. Pickering, was so interesting that I paid attention. Physics became my only good mark and so I took Physics in University. Once there, I barely passed my science courses but earned 90's in Film Making and a Fine Art Painting course. Then I discovered the campus radio station. I could blab on without interruption. Heaven! Oh yeah, and five cans of cola a day kept my motor running.

22.

Romeo

"I'm sure that I was the first kid in my class to think about sex. But I didn't have a girlfriend for a long time. A long, long time."

Sexual feelings are attached to novelty seeking and exploratory excitability, so they're a natural ingredient of daydreams. As sexual beings, our adolescence is the place to begin ones fantasy of power, in the face of powerlessness. But there is a difference between sexual imaginings and actual sexual dominance. Like many adolescents who are socially ostracized, ADDers are often relegated to the lower rungs of the social pecking order.

I was on such a low rung I didn't realize there was an order. Thank goodness I write with my right hand because my left hand was always cramped.

TMI Rick.

Oh... So this is what you were talking about in Sign 19, trouble reading social cues? Got it. I think.

23.

Loved Those *Sirens*

"I really got to know the hospital thanks to my broken bones, cuts, and sprains from my crazy stunts. At one point they took my bike away because I kept doing dangerous tricks. Oh, and ask my mom about the 'Patio Umbrella Parachute' I invented. That one even scared me."

ADHD kids have more ER visits, more head injuries, more bike accidents, and more broken bones than other children (20). It is difficult to say whether it's driven by novelty seeking, being goaded into earning peer acceptance, or really not thinking through the consequences. I know that ADHD kids seem to feel no pain when they inflict it themselves (e.g. dare-devilish stunts) but get wild when someone tries to hurt them (e.g. show them a needle). I don't think their risk taking behavior is an innate death wish; more like an eternal optimism or worse, a blind naivety.

My most serious bike accident was in broad daylight on a wide, empty, suburban street. Bob, Bruce and I are racing along and I start telling jokes… BAM! I slam into the back of a car.

The car is parked. Parked!

The only car for a half mile and I hit it! The flip side? A few years later I taught myself to ride a unicycle. "Balancing on one wheel? Now that's interesting!" Once I could do it… Bored. Moving on. Hey, there's a guitar…

24.

Child *Chimney*

"I started smoking at a really early age. Partly because it was what the other outsiders did and partly because it really made me feel better. A smoke and a coffee. Nine times a day."

There are many pseudo-attractive aspects to cigarettes: finding community amongst others who are similarly ostracized, the energizing feeling induced by nicotine, and the rebellious nature of the act. "I'm different. This proves it." But, nicotine is a gateway drug leading to other illicit substances, most commonly for ADDers, cannabis (21). Why? ADDers are often suggestible and desperate for connection, typically with the bad crowd. Since adolescence is a time of normal experimentation, it's not surprising that ADDers are at very high risk for substance use. That's why proper ADHD medication is actually protective. Their brain doesn't have to find dopamine in illicit forms.

As a teen I didn't smoke, drink or do drugs. Ever. I suspected that if I started, I wouldn't stop. After all, I was addicted to caffeinated colas. Today, recalling the gang of hard-partying outcasts I hung around with, I can see that my puritanical abstinence was my own form of rebellion; "I'm not just an outsider, I'm even different from the other outsiders." Which made me a double rebel… and the designated driver. I also refrained from promiscuity, but that wasn't my choice.

Chapter Three

Common Behaviors in ADDers

To understand the sometimes illogical behaviors of the ADDer we need to understand what drives those behaviours. The neurobiology. The wiring and chemistry.

We know that the medications doctors prescribe for ADHD tell your body to increase the level of certain hormones, namely the fight-or-flight chemicals. They are part of a class of chemical known as Catecholamines. (Pronounced Cat-A-Coal-A-Means… if you're into pronouncing things.)

The two specific ones related to ADHD are Dopamine and Noradrenaline. (And yes, Noradrenaline is related to Adrenaline.) If you don't have enough of these chemicals to transmit signals around the brain, you feel lazy, unmotivated or unable to focus.

Your brain, saddled with a deficiency of this communication fuel, decides to force the body to produce a replacement. You do things which will increase your Dopamine and Noradrenaline. (And remember, Noradrenline is related to Adrenaline.) The result? Some interesting behaviors, such as…

25.

Life at *the Edge*

"I am not reckless. Or crazy. I don't jump off the tenth floor of a building just because it exists. But I love excitement. If there's something new, interesting, exciting… I'm there!"

The ADDers brain is looking for a source to generate the chemicals it's lacking. Without medication, they may become an adrenaline junkie. The adrenaline doesn't have to originate from external events, like sex, gambling or going on a shopping spree; it could be internal, like day dreaming about sex, gambling or going on a shopping spree.

The ADHD brain seems to be low in two key chemicals, Dopamine and Noradrenaline. Basically, Dopamine makes us DO things and Noradrenaline makes us React to things. Fight or Flight. These neuro-chemicals are created by a specific metabolism that begins with the amino acid, Tyrosine. By going through some chemical changes, the Tyrosine turns to Dopamine then to Noradrenaline and then to Adrenaline (22). Though the ADHD brain is not producing enough Tyrosine, so far there is no evidence that eating foods which are rich in Tyrosine will make up for the deficiency.

I know my brain is low in something when I see a picture of Claudia Schiffer, pass out, and regain consciousness 10 hours later in a dark alleyway. Is that 'Doing?' Or 'Reacting?'

26.

Pacing to the Moon

"I get my best ideas while moving. When we're brainstorming at work I often pace or move around. If I have to sit, my brain goes haywire and my body feels like it will burst. So I'll fidget or surf the Internet. It actually helps!"

By adulthood the hyperactivity of childhood seems to abate. It may turn into an inner restlessness or nervousness. Regardless, the ADDer needs to move. Movement may very well generate the kind of chemicals their brain needs. Sit still and their brain turns off. Stuck in a chair, the adult rocks, fidgets, tilts their chair back, and as usual tips and falls.

A better strategy is to get up and pace; it burns off excess energy and actually seems to help focusing.

Now that I know what's going on, I use this restlessness to my advantage. My cell phone has a 'Voice Recorder' function, so when I'm on the move and ideas start flowing I can capture them. If I need to stand or pace during creative meetings, I do. No apologies. Admittedly, pacing can lead me to the fridge. Or the coffee machine. (Caffeine is another stimulant. Go to a Starbucks and you'll see all these Type A personalities sitting reading, actually able to focus.)

27.

Clap On, *Clap Off*

"When something has gone wrong, I am on, fully alert. However, when everything is going fine I switch off and a gorilla with jumper cables couldn't get my engine started."

An ADDer is like a light switch. There is no dimmer, no mid-range. When their brain is off, the hours seem to drag by. They can see all the things they want to do… but their mind is crushed by lethargy. Their inner voice says, "I'll get to it later".

They are up until the wee hours, but dead in the morning. Sometimes they think that a cup of coffee, a joint, or a computer game will get them in the mood. They discover leaving things to the last minute produces anxiety and a rush of adrenaline. Now they are back in the race and they zoom… if they can find the starting line.

Oh, I know this one. When I finally had everything managed, I'd take on more, to keep me juiced. Exhausting! At some point, crisis management stopped being fun. Now I break down large tasks into chunks, with short deadlines. A series of short sprints. Hey, I'm a sprinter and that's cool.

28.

Clowns are People Too

"Everyone agrees that I am a natural comedian. I was the class clown at school. Everyone laughed. But no one really wanted to be my friend."

Humor is a natural defense. But there are different kinds of humour. It starts out in childhood as being silly, 'a goof'. Later the ADDer discovers humor allows them to vent their frustrations. This veiled humor, or sarcasm, can be a useful coping strategy. But the healthiest type of humor makes others feel comfortable. Humor is also an excellent way to deal with the unresolved pain of their past. I often have patients create a joke-diary. They must look for "funny". It might be a comical moment, a joke they heard or a clip from the paper. It reminds them that the world is an absurdly funny place. Look for funny and feel good.

There's a saying that PAIN + TIME = FUNNY. In other words, "Someday we'll look back and laugh at this." Maybe it's my ADHD-fueled impatience, but 'someday' seems a long way off. Why not start laughing now? The whole world is a joke! Starting with my bank balance.

29.

7200 rice grains *in one cup!*

"I love trivia. I know lots of stuff about stuff. I can dazzle people with my knowledge of minutia. So why can't I remember the deadline for paying bills or the dates of my children's birthdays?"

ADDers love knowledge but they may not be able to separate out what is important. They want to know it all. There is a quirky power in knowing so much. They will spend countless hours surfing the web. But the triviality of some information, like the material things they own, can become another form of clutter.

I'm a demon at Trivial Pursuit. During Jeopardy I'm yelling out answers like an auctioneer, and my wife is stunned, "How did you know that?" And honestly, sometimes I have no idea. I also have no idea where I put my car keys.

30.

Later, Dude!

"I procrastinate. I will find something to do, anything at all, to avoid the things I have to do. There is this eternal optimism that somehow it will all be okay... in the face of mounting debt, delinquency, shame, chaos and scandal."

 There are many reasons why ADHD individuals procrastinate: passive resistance; a lack of understanding of priorities; a poor sense of time; mental fatigue; an avoidance of success or failure; or maybe just a means of escaping judgment.

Regardless, something is stuck. Their brain lacks the fuel it needs to wake up and get moving. They delay important tasks. The deadlines loom closer. Their fear mounts. Under this pressure their brain finally wakes up. The problem is that it is often too late. Or else everyone around them has to deal with the crisis. ADDers can make very frustrating bosses.

 When I'd rather lick sandpaper than do something I need to do, I make it a game. A challenge. A race. I focus on the reward.

Create rewards that matter to you. And when you're done, celebrate your success. If you're living with an ADDer, praise the bejeebers out of every accomplishment. We love it.

31.

Tongue *Tipped*

"I'm doing a chore and I realize I need a tool from downstairs. I go to fetch it. In the 10 seconds it takes to reach the basement, I've completely forgot what I came for, what I was doing, and why I needed it."

An ADDer may have a problem with Working Memory (WM). Think of WM as the grocery list memory (23). This the throw away memory: once the short-term goal is completed the information can be expunged. Toss it or risk cluttering the brain. For those with a deficit of WM, electronic organizers can be a godsend. Even without gadgets, WM can be helped using simple strategies such as creating a pneumonic, or remembering the context of the situation.

Here's a naughty trick: You are with someone and an acquaintance whose name you forget approaches. Whip out your cell phone as though it's vibrating, and tell the two people, "Introduce yourselves." Then pretend you're taking a call. Just don't get so caught up in your fake call that you miss their names when they introduce themselves! A less naughty trick is to repeat someone's name as they say it, and use it two or three times as you talk, so you remember it. Even better, introduce the person to someone else. Saying their name aloud makes it stick.

What's-his-name taught me this. You know… Uh… Dad.

32.

Mindless Miracle

"I get my best ideas when I am in the shower or knitting or cutting vegetables. It is as if I need to keep my body busy doing something and it frees up the creative part of my mind."

When the ADDer's mind is on autopilot, their brain goes into free floating thinking which can be very stimulating. However the tendency to become lost in thought can sabotage their time management. They become lost in a fantasy world and, WHAM, an hour slips past; their body is going through the motions but their brain is somewhere else, lost on trivialities.

Sure, we are called space cadet, scattered or absent minded professor. But we also get called creative, cross-disciplinary and able to see things from a unique perspective. It's a fine line. The point of taking on your ADHD is to discover where that line is. And it's different for each of us.

33.

Wikipedia *Sex*

"I could spend all day on information gathering at the library or on Wikipedia. It is orgasmic to find something fascinating, let alone the occasional pornographic reference."

Wikipedia promises a new adventure on every page. The ADDer may have gone there for a simple fact but each link, highlighted in blue, is a potential gold mine that must be explored. This unending labyrinth can trap a divergent thinker: someone who thinks broadly rather than details or specifics. You could say ADDers can see the forest but not the trees. For the same reason, they tend to do well with puzzles and problem solving (other people's problems; not their own).

At University I'd go to the library to study but end up strolling up and down the shelves, pulling out every book that caught my fancy. I remember that's where I discovered a "Faggot" is a "bundle of sticks." The upside was, I learned a little bit about almost everything. The downside was the University didn't award a degree for that.

34.

Cool in a Crisis

"I'm really great in a crisis. When 'it' hits the proverbial fan, I feel like I am alert, in charge and... me."

Though I can lose my cool over small things, in a real crisis I can be super focused. No voices of doubt. Time slows down and everything is clear. Several police officers and military people I know talk openly about their ADHD. What overwhelms others just wakes us up.

In a 9/11 world, I look to the ADDer to save my life. They're calm in a crisis. But when everything is calm, they are in crisis!

Remember, this is about neurology. The frontal lobes are the last part of the brain to mature. And the ADHD lobes don't work as efficiently as everyone else's. Some excellent Positron Emission Tomography (PET) scans done by Alan Zametkin at the NIMH show that the frontal lobes of an ADDer don't light up with activity. (24). More evidence that the ADHD brain is different. What is even more interesting is that when medications are given, these areas seem to become near normal (25). Unfortunately, the technology in PET, SPECT, fMRI and other imaging studies has not advanced enough that one can make a diagnosis or draw specific conclusions. (Despite what some may claim). So keep your money in your pocket.

35.

Spidey *Senses*

"Sometimes I'm totally clairvoyant. I feel things instinctively. I can sense tension or romance the moment I walk into a situation. I've predicted the future before it happened. Really! I don't tell people this because they think I am psychotic not Psychic."

This perception of being able to sense the future seems odd but perhaps the ADDer is simply taking in more information. Most people's brains filter out all the irrelevant distractions; they edit out the noise. The ADHD brain doesn't. Sometimes what seems irrelevant is actually important, so they may sense things others miss, and therefore make connections others might not.

They come to odd, but in hindsight logical conclusions. It is not clairvoyance, just a sophisticated form of information deduction.

I have moments of intuition but most of the time, the lack of filtering is not an asset. A voice down the hall, a passing siren or the tag on my shirt collar is distracting. However, stimulate my brain with an interesting topic or with a stimulant medication and my filter snaps on. Then, I can shut out the distractions and hyper focus. Less activity and more productivity with just as much creativity. (That's catchy! I should trademark that. Or put it on fridge magnets.)

36.

The *Joy* of Joysticks

"I can't have ADHD because I can super focus during an action film or while playing a video game. Or ideally, when I'm playing a video game based on an action film. I develop laser eyes, super focus, and thumbs of steel."

Most people can focus on passively stimulating things like videos and TV's. But to the ADDer, they're much more seductive. They can feel like a drug. With similar cravings and withdrawal symptoms. Computer monitors and TV screens literally awaken their brain to full power. The problem is that things that are not stimulating, like reading, will seem so much harder by comparison.

I decided to abstain from playing video games after realizing I was waking up with a Repetitive Strain Injury from doing Tetris in my sleep. Mind you all the pillows were neatly interlocked.

Chapter Four

Common Misbehaviors

Ever wonder if ADHD is Nature vs. Nurture? We know the ADD brain responds to stimulation. It learns to seek out excitement. To roam and imagine. As if standing at the edge of a cliff and seeing things that no one else can see. Nature.

If that capacity is encouraged by unconditional love, enveloped by structure and excited with passion, then the ADDer becomes a powerhouse. Nurture.

If it is not, then the ADDer is standing at the edge of disaster. That's the unfortunate reality of many an ADDer, a bad environment.

The common ADHD behaviors described in this chapter make it clear why this is considered a Disorder. When nurture fails and things go wrong…

37.

ADD = *ADDiction*

"I've actually avoided going into casinos, because I suspect the thing that 'stays in Vegas' would be me. I have a difficult time saying no, even though I know something might be bad for me."

The Nucleus Accumbens (NA) is a deep part of the brain that gives us that "win" feeling (26). This is the GO! signal. It is the voice of eternal optimism, even in the face of overwhelming odds that should tell the ADDer to say no. Instead they say, yes. Once they feel the rush of Dopamine, they will want it again. And again. ADDers are at risk for addictions because they can't moderate these competing signals. ADDers can be addicted to most anything. For example, the rate of ADHD among Pathological Gamblers is as high as 40% (27).

Addiction used to mean cigarettes, drugs, or alcohol. Now it includes work, sex, video games, energy drinks, exercise, Internet surfing, shopping, coffee, or anything that you crave. My addiction of choice was work. So why aren't I rich?!

38.

The *Humpty-Dumpty* Syndrome

"I have a metal pin in my leg from the motorcycle accident, and one in my wrist from skateboarding and a plate in my hip when I tried snowmobiling in July."

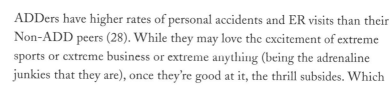 ADDers have higher rates of personal accidents and ER visits than their Non-ADD peers (28). While they may love the excitement of extreme sports or extreme business or extreme anything (being the adrenaline junkies that they are), once they're good at it, the thrill subsides. Which means they must keep pushing the limits farther to produce the high. Unfortunately, they may push so hard that they exceed the limit and hurt themselves, or their family, or the entire economy!

Who needs extreme sports to get hurt? I've stubbed my toes so many times that I wear steel-toed slippers. After breaking 3 wristwatches by whacking my arm on tables or door frames, I bought a pocket watch. Since treating my ADHD that clumsiness has diminished. When I do trip over a sidewalk crack or gouge my shin on the metal bed frame it's because I'm lost in thought again. Who needs a Tibetan meditation gong when I have a Sears bed frame that reminds me to 'be here now'.

39.

Bored Member

"Life is boring! I go through job after job because I can't stand the mundane existence. And when the going gets tough, I get distracted, or tired, and give up. It's happened so often, that I'm really touchy about it."

ADDers are more likely to have been fired and have frequent job changes (29). They are also less likely to maximize their earnings compared to their peers, largely because they can't stick to any one job long enough (30). Being easily bored, they jump to a fresh situation, convinced the grass will be greener. It never is. Their work experience has breadth but not depth. The ADDer is the jack-of-all-trades who never commits to mastering one. Or is fired before they can master it.

I didn't change jobs, I just kept on adding more. I felt like I had to overdo everything to keep excited about life. As every workaholic discovers, excessive work leads to other problems. Like no family to spend my earnings on. It went to the divorce lawyers instead. So now, when I work, I work. When I play, I leave work at work and I play full tilt. When I rest and recharge, I have to commit to it… No guilt, no Internet, no cell phone… A real break. It's a completely weird experience and I have to fight the urge to check Ashton Kutcher's Tweets every three minutes. And I don't even know who Ashton is. Seriously, who is she?

40.

The *Larry King* Effect

"I'm on my third marriage. And it's not going well. I drive her crazy. This woman who loved to be with me has turned into someone who just nags, judges, complains and is constantly negative."

ADDers have a much higher rate of divorce (31). Some common reasons include: 1) A higher rate of other, additional mental health issues; 2) Ineffective skills in conflict resolution (a remnant from childhood); 3) A tendency to highly expressed emotions (more than, "Hey, we're a loud family."); 4) The stress of raising one or more ADHD children; 5) The relationship becomes stale and boring; 6) Constantly at odds because they are opposite in temperament; 7) Lack of trust; 8) Choosing a partner who is the extension of the "bad parent" from childhood; or 9) Yet another complex social interaction that they have no time to understand or manage

When I tuned out during conversations, my wife assumed that I cared more about the football game on TV in the next room. No. It's just what grabbed my attention. Undiagnosed ADHD sabotages relationships. Even with a reliable diagnosis, a relationship is challenging, but at least we have a chance to avoid the moral judgments and deal with it.

BTW, it's shocking how often our partners suspect we have ADHD before we do. Sure, we may wonder, and consider the possibility... but then we think, "Oh, look! Cows!"

41.

Will It *Fall Off?*

"OK, I'll admit to the occasional paid sexual encounter. And yeah, I have had my share of sexually transmitted diseases. I thank God that I haven't had AIDS... yet."

ADDers have 2 to 4 times the rates of Sexually Transmitted Diseases (STD's) (32). While ADDers are sexually active at an earlier age than their peers, they are not usually involved in steady relationships (33).

The restlessness and novelty seeking of ADHD undermines long-term commitments, and even family planning. Not surprisingly, they have twice the rate of unwanted pregnancies, and overwhelmed by life, often give up the child for adoption (34). The result is that I see a lot of adoptees who have ADHD.

I need physical intimacy as much as the next person. Especially if that person is Casanova. I avoided STD's during my teenage years through a clever strategy of being a shy, pimply nerd. Okay, maybe it wasn't a strategy so much as a series of bad wardrobe choices and ineffective acne medication. But it worked. Dammit.

42.

Hole-y Pocket

"I've been through one bankruptcy and I am heading for a second one. I admit that I make impulsive purchases. But hey, I'm not buying a new car every month."

Money is a problem. ADDers have a much higher rate of bankruptcies due to mismanaging businesses (35). As well, untreated ADDers earn, on average, $10,000 less than their Non-ADD peers (36). They also indulge in endless trivial spending. Buying one energy drink seems insignificant, but if they add up what it costs them over a year… Of course, that would require keeping receipts. Because ADDers have trouble delaying gratification (i.e. being able to save), a credit card plus the Home Shopping channel makes it too easy to feel the euphoria of desiring and scoring a bargain. Actually owning what they bought? That feels anticlimactic and boring.

I've heard so many entrepreneurs with ADHD admit, "After I get a new business running I hand it off to someone who will manage it or I drive it into the ground." Why? We come up with a cool idea. We start it up. There are a ton of problems. We can be good at solving problems. When it's finally humming along… we grow bored. So we tinker, add complications, take risks.

The lesson? Once it's working, hand it off. Or have someone who will yank it away from you and tell you to go start something new. New?! Oh boy, we like new!

43.

Lead Foot

"I feel focused when I speed. I know I scare other drivers but it's more dangerous if I am going the speed limit. I stop paying attention and drift out of my lane, or miss my exit."

ADDers are nine times more likely to have had multiple car accidents (37) And more likely to be at fault. They are prone to more at-fault accidents, speeding infractions, license suspensions and parking violations (38).

Here are some of the possible reasons behind this: 1) They feel more alert at a higher speed; 2) They fear they will disappoint someone or miss an opportunity if they are late (which they usually are anyway); 3) They believe their driving skills are above average; 4) Rushing urgently feels familiar; 5) They have never paused to fully appreciate the dangers; 6) They find traffic rules unfairly rigid; or 7) They believe they are smarter than the police (even after they get caught).

At the Go Kart track I rule. Yet on real roads in a real car, I've had six accidents. But ALWAYS at low speed. Cause slow is boring, and I'm not really paying attention. Oh yeah, and remember that ADHD runs in families? Well, two months after my son got his license he drove into a parked car. But hey, he is great at Go Karts. We just have to ask my wife to drive us to the track.

44.

The *Tiger Woods* Condition

"Whenever I had an affair I was always afraid they'd go wacko on me like in the movie, Fatal Attraction. You'd think my fear would keep my eyes from wandering but the danger made it more addictive."

The ADDer must master situations of risk. There are four steps they need to learn. 1) Delay one's urges by creating time for their brain to get the "no" word working. For example, a TV addict is less likely to spend another evening channel surfing if they store the TV in the garage behind some boxes. They'll realize, it's "Not worth the effort". 2) Avoid risk situations. For example, if they avoid the mall they may be less likely to get caught shoplifting. 3) Be Accountable. They should always feel like someone is watching. For example, Tiger Woods should have given his cell phone access code to his wife to deter him from straying. 4) They should Defer the "no signal" to someone else. For example, having someone they trust handle their paycheck so the ADDer isn't tempted to squander the rent money on frivolities.

Delay, Avoid, Accountable, Defer. Call it the DAAD principle.

The DAAD Principle could be applied to every misbehaviour in this Chapter! For me, DAAD comes in the form of a loving spouse. A positive, encouraging partner makes it easy to avoid risks.

45.

Dumb Delinquent

"In Grade 7 I was caught stealing. It wasn't my idea, really; I was acting as the lookout. OK, I have been caught for cannabis possession and yes, I have been charged with drunk driving. And yes, I know better. But hey, it's just small stupid stuff."

 Sure, ADDers are at higher risk for criminal behavior (39), but here's the good news; they may be able to replace an impulsive urge with the opposite action. For example, ask a Fire Fighter if they were ever a fire bug as a child! A kid with a Conduct Disorder grows up to become a police officer or an attorney. The drug addict becomes a drug counselor. The rape victim is now a social worker. The kid who hated school becomes a dedicated teacher.

 Or perhaps, the shy, bookish, neurotic nebbish becomes the brilliant and much beloved comedian (Blush).

 Either a comedian or an accountant.

 Really? Wow, that was close!

 By the way, your accountant called about a tax audit.

46.

Wild Man

"People make me furious. During my divorce I just wanted to punish her. In small claims court I wanted to see my business partner suffer. Once when I was so enraged I was charged with assault. I oughta keep a lawyer on retainer."

An ADHD child suffers. The world forces them to bury their anger. Years later, in adulthood, if the ADDer is made to feel like a child again, Pandora's box opens up. Feelings of being victimized resurface as explosive rage. Low self esteem makes it easier to blame others rather than take responsibility for their actions (40). Many patients who come to see me about ADHD realize that anger is the impairing symptom that's ruling their lives, destroying their relationships and hurting their children.

I used to savour my anger, nurturing it, watering it with righteousness, feeding it with justifications. I'd spin huge and complex revenge fantasies, fueled by my sense of injustice. Of course, I'd be nice and polite in person. I avoided getting punched in the face by being two-faced.

The documentary ADD & Loving It?! started out as my way of showing up everyone who had dismissed my ADHD. Of course, anger isn't sustainable and I found better, positive motivators, to finish the film. Like getting paid.

47.

Recreational Abuse

"Why is cannabis illegal? Makes no sense. I usually use grass and alcohol with my friends who, incidentally, are a lot like me. My doc said I had to get off the weed before he would treat my ADHD. Yea, right. It's the only thing that helps."

The drugs of choice for the unmedicated ADDer are cigarettes, cannabis, cocaine, alcohol, caffeine and energy drinks. The risk of substance abuse starts at puberty. There is considerable evidence that adequate treatment of ADHD protects the adolescent or adult from abusing other drugs (41). On our website, TotallyADD.com, Dr. Sam Chang, an addiction specialist from Calgary, Canada explains that about 10% of normal teenagers are heavy marijuana users but among ADHD teenagers it is 30%, three times as many! With effective ADHD medication, that rate drops to about 12%. Not quite as low as their Non-ADHD peers, but close! The fact is, people with ADHD will find something that works. No matter what the cost.

So many creative people suspect they have ADHD after seeing our documentary, ADD & Loving It?! What's telling is how many use cannabis. And it's beyond recreational. Many swear they need to self-medicate to be able to write, play guitar, draw, or whatever. One comedian I know, who was properly diagnosed, and tried ADHD medication told me his creativity was undiminished. And his productivity soared. Who knew!? Well, I did, cause the same thing happened to me.

48.

Little *Bastards*

"I got pregnant when I was 18. After a one-night stand. It was so stupid, but what could I do? I felt like I was a nine-year old raising a one-year old"

 I remember being 15, 16, 17. Vaguely. The risk of pregnancy? Not on my lust-clouded, hormone-soaked, teeny-bopper craving radar. I was like a salmon, eager to spawn and die. If I'd actually managed to convince a girl to go along with me I'm sure it would have been awesome. For me anyway.

 There are further risk factors beyond higher rates of unplanned pregnancy. Mothers who have ADHD children are more likely to have smoked during their pregnancies (42). It's like bathing the fetus in high adrenaline and that affects it's development. Other studies have shown ADHD parents are likely to be more abusive, more likely to be single parents and more likely to have poor parenting skills (43). Adding to this misery, there's often ambivalence to the child in the first place (i.e. the child's father was abusive or absent). As the child grows they remind the mother of the louse who fathered the child and ruined their life. The mother's unresolved anger at the absent father is taken out on the innocent child.

 Yikes!

ADD STOLE MY CAR KEYS

Chapter Five

Signs of Inattention in Adults

One of the core impairments of ADHD is Inattention. We said this before, but you may not have been paying attention. Remember, if you only have problems with Inattention, (i.e. as a child you were the quiet daydreamer), then you are called 'The Predominantly Inattentive Subtype'. In lay terms, ADD.

More common are individuals who have problems with Inattention combined with Hyperactivity and Impulsivity. Thus the name, 'The Predominantly Combined Subtype". By adulthood these Combined Subtype kids usually, but not always, move towards the Inattentive Subtype. In other words, the Hyperactivity and Impulsivity evolve. The ADDer learns to control themselves and 'behave.' Somewhat.

For both groups, the struggle over Inattention is fundamental. And it's more complex than mere 'Distractibility'.

That's because there are different facets of Inattention: 1) Finding the right thing to focus on ("Look, the whole house is a mess!"); 2) Prioritizing ("Taxes? But my shoes need polishing."); 3) Staying with it ("Oh look! A Blue Jay!"); 4) Shifting focus if something more urgent arises ("Don't bother me, I'm working!"); 5) Over focusing, or hyper-focusing. ("I forgot to stop and eat dinner!").

This chapter describes how the core impairment of Inattention presents itself in adults.

49.

Frantic *Frenzy*

"Guests are coming over, so I vacuum. Then I remember, 'We'll need chairs.' So I stop vacuuming to fetch some. But along the way, I notice the messy closet. I never finish vacuuming, but the closet, which the guests won't see, looks great."

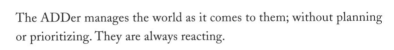

The ADDer manages the world as it comes to them; without planning or prioritizing. They are always reacting.

As well, everything has the same value and therefore everything seems equally important. This can look like perfectionism or excessive rigidity; it's actually more of a lack of spatial understanding and how to prioritize tasks. They are busy all right, but there's precious little evidence of their full day's effort.

But geez, Dr. J, it feels efficient. I finally decide to do my taxes, but mixed in with my receipts are photos, coupons, birthday cards and 100 reminders. Soon, I'm on a bigger mission, sorting all of my paper! At long last, I'll be organized! Hooray! But, at some point I end up super-focused on some trivial task, such as mounting memorabilia in scrapbooks... My taxes? Well, they are started. But never finished. There's no sense of progress, no satisfaction because nothing ever gets checked off the list.

50.

"I just *had* them a minute ago!!!"

"I can never find my keys. Or my purse. Or my umbrella. I have tried all kinds of tricks, like an umbrella stand and hooks for my keys. But still, things are never where they are supposed to be. It's f*$?%ing gremlins."

The ADDer can't remember where they left their keys because they were not really 'present' when they put them down. They were thinking about dinner or replaying a conversation from work. They lack what is called Presence of Mind. The lost keys symbolize their lack of mindfulness. The lack of control is frustrating, and success around this issue is very much about habit construction.

My wife put a funky antique ashtray near our front door. When I arrive home I toss my keys, phone, change, wallet and sunglasses into it. As I leave the next morning, I load up again. Foolproof, right? Until winter arrived. There were so many boots by the door, we moved the ashtray back a few feet. Still there, just not in plain sight. Sure enough, I sailed past, oblivious. Next morning my keys are on the microwave, my wallet is on the coffee table, and somehow my sunglasses end up in the shower?!

51.

Promptly One Hour Late

"I am late for everything. Appointments. Meetings. Weddings. I was late for a dinner party, but I didn't feel bad, because I knew they hadn't served the food yet. Then I was embarrassed to find out they'd held off eating while they waited for me."

The ADDer gets into trouble because: 1) They hate arriving early and being bored. 2) They misjudge the steps required to get to someplace. They don't allow time to dress, shave, wash, find keys, find the invite, get directions, deal with traffic, or find parking. This kind of planning is called Linear Thinking. 3) They are the master of excuses so they have a false belief they can 'get away with it.' 4) They expect people to understand and make allowances, and feel incensed when they don't.

It used to be I'd arrive at a meeting and I'd rhyme off all the reasons I was late: A huge traffic jam (which I took a picture of, for proof). A slow moving funeral procession (and I happened to know the deceased, for proof). A thousand chickens crossing the road to get to the other side (and I have a box of KFC, for proof).

Now, I aim to arrive early. And if I actually do, I gas up the car, tidy the trunk, call a friend, neck with my wife... often all at the same time.

52.

Death By *Lists*

"I have drawn up a million lists and I have never, ever finished one of them. I don't know why I bother."

Making lists gives a sense of control, a feeling that we are creating limits. But ADDers usually take on too much, and end up creating huge lists. They fantasize, "If everything goes perfectly I could finish all of this today." But the list is far too ambitious, sucking out whatever hope they had of getting ahead. Or simply caught up. They set themselves up for yet another disheartening failure. To feel productive they may 'cherry pick' their list, doing fast, fun tasks first, but the big things stay on the list day after day, a perpetual reminder of their incompetence.

For years, I'd start my day asking myself, "What needs doing?" Then I'd list 438 tasks. That took two hours. Realizing I should focus on what was urgent, I edited the list down to a manageable 369 tasks. But even just those would take a month to complete, so… Heck, I will plan the whole month! Good for me. By the end of the day, I'd have laid out a schedule that rivaled the plans for D-Day. Now, I have one thing a day on my To-Do List. One! The most urgent. The big dragon that needs slaying. I can't choose something else from the list, so I get it done.

You'll find more tips for getting things done at TotallyADD.com. Whole lists of tips! Ha ha ha!

53.

Grey Matter *Disjunction*

"I can read the same page five times and have no idea what it said. I mean, I am reading; my eyes move and the pages turn. But zero recall. Even if there's not a lot of text. For example, I've had to reread the caption on a cartoon twice just to get the joke!"

 ADDers have a disconnect between 'decoding' and 'storage'. The information may be stored but they can't figure out where; a task called Information Retrieval. One strategy is to read aloud into a tape recorder, creating a personal Audio Book. Later, if they become stuck, listen back to the tape. Another tactic is to read with the idea of giving themselves a quiz afterwards. Or reading a story as if they will have to retell it later to someone else. All of these contexts transform how they attack reading, engaging the mind and making things stick.

 Audio books rule! They can be pricey, but most libraries loan them. With audio books I can learn something while I'm driving, instead of just cursing aggressive soccer-moms in giant SUVs. On a long car trip we all listen. Comedy albums are great too!

54.

Heaps of Fun; *Nothing Done!*

"This is where I do my crafts. The table is somewhere under those heaps of fabric. This is a quilt I started. Here's another I'm almost done. This is a baby outfit I started sewing for Melanie. But she's 21 now. I'll finish it for the baby she's expecting..."

Prioritize! To do this, the ADDer will have to limit their choices. How? With the word NO Unfortunately, ADDers have a tendency to say YES, especially if they fear they will let someone down. Could it also be boredom that has them jump to what is new, novel, and fresh? Perhaps.

The solution? Focusing on the finish line. They need to imagine the relief they'll enjoy when it's done. And when it is done, they must pause and savor their success.

I was a Yes Man. I said, "Yeah. Sure. I can do that!" The other person was always delighted. They had that 'Christmas present' look and I loved feeling helpful and appreciated! Of course, two weeks later when I hadn't delivered, I'd quietly disappear or hide out. Brutal. Now, I'm training myself to say, "Let me check my schedule and get back to you tomorrow." No one seems to mind. And reality has time to set in so I can honestly say, "I'd love to, but..."

55.

I *Escaped* Through the Window

"All through school, I daydreamed. Staring out the window, or gazing around the classroom. Sometimes I'd doodle, or draw magical worlds that were a hundred times more interesting than anything the teacher presented. I have fifty 'Calvin & Hobbes' comic strips above my desk. Calvin is so me."

Daydreaming is like an inner form of distraction. Hard to turn off something so enjoyable. ADHD/ADD kids have significant on-task problems. There's a big difference! No wonder their marks are so low. They are busy somewhere else. No wonder they assume they are the dummy in the family. Or, if tests show they have a high IQ, then they must be, "lazy, weak-willed, stubborn or don't care."

This was so me. At university I calculated how much tuition I was paying for each hour of class. It was a lot! Since I wanted to get my parent's moneys worth, I sat up front so I would focus on the teacher and blackboards. Rather than take notes by rote, I translated everything the Profs said into my own words. And I forced myself to ask at least one question every class, so then I had to be listening. Otherwise I'd be asking dumb questions. The result of these strategies? I was actually engaged.

56.

"Exactly *When* was Photoshop™ Invented?"

"I've found photographs of myself at a party and I have zero memory of being there. I'll wonder, 'Did someone Photoshop me in? Or, maybe I did something horrible and blocked it out of my memory!' Frankly, that is a real possibility!"

With the passage of time, all childhood memories grow fuzzy, but when there is pain in those memories, the brain builds up a protective barrier. But photographs are usually taken at fun moments, and contain good memories. So in the example above, this isn't about 'repressed memories'. It's about Mindfulness. When the photograph was taken, the ADDer was a million miles away, lost in thought. No wonder they don't remember being there; they weren't! The solution? ADDers can keep a diary to record their best memories (just like a photo album). They should record the highlights. They should also include any memorable, vivid or emotional details; we call this Associative Memory because it creates a context to anchor the memory.

At my 25th High School reunion a woman shouted, "Rick! It's me! Ellen Kwan!" Instantly a flood of memories exploded in my head. As I was writing out my E-mail address for her she shouted, "You still hold your pen funny and stick out your tongue when you write!" All evening long, one memory would trigger a dozen more memories for everyone else. Frightening. In a good way.

57.

Great Ideas that *Never Happen*

"I have great ideas! But once the initial enthusiasm passes, I stall. My mind reels when faced with a million steps that need doing. I end up paralyzed by, 'Now what?' Eventually I have nine things started, then feel overwhelmed and run out of energy, having completed nothing."

It's bad enough that lists will kill, but the ADDer faces another lethal challenge: their inability to prioritize. If all tasks appear to be equally urgent, it's easy to scan that to-do list and avoid the important, but unpleasant, tasks. Perhaps this passive delaying avoids some pain. But by procrastinating, their angst grows. The solution? Pick two major priorities per day; critical tasks that move life forward. Completing these two projects in the morning, while their brain has just been rested and is at its best is empowering and makes the rest of the day feel easy.

I'm big on 'Chunking' tasks. I'm even chunky-looking. For example, exercise is a major priority. But going jogging strikes me as a huge commitment. So I'll ask, can I do one small thing, like find my running shoes? Sure. So I do. Once my shoes are on, I figure I might as well run to the corner. When I get there, I think, heck, one more block...

These small victories are like potato chips; when I have one I crave another. Whereas waiting to feel motivated to go jogging... it'll never happen. Trust me.

58.

Eight Power Drills

"I saw this amazing tool at the store. I knew my husband would love one. When I got home and showed it to him he was confused. I forgot that I already bought him one last year. I was going to return the new one, but I misplaced the receipt."

 Buying something they have already bought, or giving someone the same gift, or telling someone the same story again and again, are all typical of ADDers. Sure, as anyone grows older, their life's memories, experiences, and responsibilities start to clog up the grey matter. But the ADDer's forgetfulness has been there since childhood.

They need to simplify their life and unload the clutter. They should start with the things they have accumulated. Donating extra belongings to charity creates space in their mind and their life.

 Yep, I will buy something and then realize I already own one. So I do a kind of weird re-gifting and give the second one to the kids or a friend. The good news is, when I give the second one away, I can brag, "It's great. I own one myself."

59.

Yeast? It said *yeast?*

"When I try something new I always make dumb little mistakes. I saw a show about baking homemade bread and decided try it. It was a lot of fun, but the bread was like a lead pancake. My spouse pointed out that I had missed, 'Add in the yeast'. Oops!"

ADDers tend to make small mistakes because they skim while reading. They should be tested for a Reading Comprehension problem, Dyslexia or another Learning Disorder. These are far more common amongst ADDers than their Non-ADD peers (44). We'll talk more about this in Chapter 7. The ADDer can compensate for their tendency to miss details by clearly numbering and checking off each step as they do it, or laying the recipe out on a large, easy to read card.

Or letting someone else cook. That works for me! Another trick is to cook with a friend. My wife tracks where we are in the recipe and delegates steps to me: kneading dough, measuring flour, scarfing down raisins and cleaning the spatula with my tongue, chin and shirt.

60.

Home*fun?*

"I hated school. I did what I found interesting and avoided the rest. Homework? I could never get into it. Earning high marks didn't excite me. Now, as an adult, my routine paperwork just doesn't happen. It wouldn't be so bad if I didn't care, but it's always there, in the background as another nagging worry."

If teachers had called it "Homefun" rather than "Homework" the ADDer would have been all over it. ADDers love fun! But the education system promotes an important concept: work comes first and fun has to wait. ADHD kids resist that truth. Once they are grown up and working, they should find ways to make work fun. A challenge. Even a game.

At some point the work has to be done. Even in the Creative Arts success is 5% inspiration and 95% perspiration. Creativity counts for zilch if it stays in my head. My best ideas will remain ideas without deadlines. When I started in radio and television I had to deliver a half-hour of new comedy skits every week. No matter what. I was forced to be creative… and to my amazement, I produced. Ultimately everything—work, home life, parenting, friendships—are all about doing the work and delivering.

Chapter Six

Signs of Hyperactivity & Impulsivity

The ADHD stereotype is a rowdy red-headed boy. Like Dennis the Menace. They're bouncing off the walls and always talking, frustrating the teacher and authorities. Alas, unlike Bart Simpson, who can get his classmates laughing along with him, most ADHD kids are not popular; their peers find them annoying too.

By adulthood, the obvious bouncing off the walls tends to disappear. Internalized into a constant restlessness.

They sit in meetings, nodding and smiling, while their mind zooms along like a Ferrari on ice. Their Hyperactivity turns into intense impatience, agitation and anxiety. A kind of whirling dynamo, an internal tornado, that can never relax. Even on vacation.

Warning: you may read through this chapter and go, "Huhn?" That's okay. It could just mean you have the Purely Inattentive Subtype.

61.

Motor Mouthing

"Being a chatterbox is great at work, because I'm in sales. But at a party, or with my kids… I find it really difficult to just listen and not interrupt. And I hate it."

Man, that was me. Dominating conversations. I can still go there if I'm not careful. Now I've learned to pause. First, I start with the headline, "We've just been to San Francisco." If the person expresses interest I add, "The food was wonderful, but the most amazing thing was the tour of Alcatraz." Then if they show interest, "Really? The Prison? Neat.", that's my signal to keep going.

An even better strategy? Ask questions. Like "Have you been to San Francisco?" Their story is way more interesting to me because it's new. Listening… who knew?!

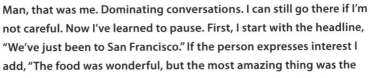

Dominating conversations or interrupting could be the result of a number of factors: 1) The ADDer's memory for trivial information is so short, they need to blurt out what they want to say before they forget; 2) Their brain thinks so fast that their mouth struggles to keep up, causing verbal diarrhea (This is different than manic-type pressured speech); 3) They are impatient or bored, so they rush conversations; 4) They need to explain every detail to ensure the listener truly understands. However the listener just tunes out; or 5) A monologue makes them the centre of attention.

But like Rick suggests, active listening is so important.

62.

Carpet Burns

"The carpet near our phone is worn out because I pace when I talk. It's the same at work. Clearly, the cordless phone was invented by an ADDer."

ADDers commonly report that they focus better when they are moving. They may be right! It's as if there is a motor inside of them that is constantly racing. By having an outlet to burn off excess energy, they may be able to focus better. In situations where they can't pace, perhaps a dinner with their in-laws or a very long movie, the restlessness can become painful.

One of my patients found a clever way to cope; he removed the chairs from his office and raised his desk up on stacks of bricks. Then he converted his phone to a Bluetooth and works standing up! His only complaint? Pacing in circles made him dizzy.

Benjamin Franklin showed all the signs of ADHD, and he worked standing up. Try it. It's amazing. Or try a Pilates Ball instead of an office chair. You can burn off excess energy and build core muscle strength while you argue with your cell phone provider about your $800 phone bill. (Or is that last part just me?)

63.

Tonsil Toes

"I tend to put my foot in my mouth. I blurt things out, or say something judgmental and not realize I've gone too far. I'm also terrible at keeping secrets. That's cost me a few friendships."

ADDers may think they're being funny but sometimes they are simply tactless. They justify their barbs by claiming they speak the truth. Perhaps. But a common social component is missing. This social awkwardness is long standing and goes all the way back into childhood. It can be mistaken for Asperger's Syndrome but ADDers have normal eye contact and normal speech. They just don't filter what they say.

I have been known to take a joke too far, five or six times a day. Everyone is laughing, I take it farther and farther until the laughter turns to, "Eww! Gross!" People who know me are rarely offended, but others may not get my humor or think I am loud, obnoxious, silly, irritating, a cross-dresser... I'm not... not really. See for yourself at "http://www. thefrantics.com". I'm the one in the dress.

64.

Monkey Hands

"I will be watching TV, or in a conversation, unaware that I'm rattling my pocket change. If we're heading to a big social function my wife says, 'Coins and keys, please.' And I hand them over. She's like airport security; strict, but there to protect me."

Because their brain has trouble filtering all the incoming signals, ADDers can have difficulty discerning where their body is, spatially. So they move. Why? Well, try this experiment: Concentrate on your right big toe for a few seconds. Now wiggle it and notice that it is easier to feel where it is. Wiggling produces stronger feedback signals, making it easier to sense one's body. ADDers have to move, rock or fidget, otherwise they can't feel their body. It can be annoying to others, but it's more than simply tics or bad habits. They actually have a better self awareness when they move.

In a meeting, I'm either a huge contribution, or a constant distraction. I doodle, fidget with pens, or twist paperclips into sculptures. If I'm smart, I bring a magic trick along and practice sleight of hand under the table so no one notices.

65.

Conversation *Bully*

"I have this nasty habit of not letting people finish sentences. I desperately want them to get to the point. I signal them to 'hurry up and finish' by shifting, frowning, sighing, nodding fast or checking my watch. Or I won't wait, and I'll interrupt with something way more interesting."

Impatience comes in many forms and interrupting is common. Don't confuse this with say, a married couple who, with their close connection, are able to finish each other's sentences. The ADDer wants others to go straight from A right to Z, skipping the steps in between. Ironically, when it's their turn to speak they have a problem with verbosity, filling in everything from A to Z.

They may be 'Overly Inclusive', adding endless, unnecessary details. They may be 'Circumstantial', taking a roundabout way to reach their point. They may be 'Tangential', wandering off topic, then asking, "What was I talking about again?"

Small talk? "Blah, blah, blah about the weather or the traffic?" Spare me! I want to get to the 'interesting' stuff. Or at least, what interests me. As for what Dr. J called being 'Overly Inclusive', 'Circumstantial' or 'Tangential', that's not me. In fact, the first time we went to the Bahamas, in 1988...

66.

Post *Dramatic* Disorder

"I have a dramatic flair. When things happen to me, it is always something huge, outrageous, or incredible! I relish being the centre of attention. I love to Twitter. Half my tweets contain 'OMG'. I have to cut back, because I'm up to 3,000 tweets a month, but I can't help it. People need to know about me!"

ADDers who struggle with impulsiveness often wear their hearts on their sleeves. They can be loud and emotional, overreacting to situations. Their moods may switch rapidly, from absolute rage to, "So, what's for dinner?" Friends and family are bewildered and confused. Not surprisingly these wild swings may be mistaken for Bipolar Disorder (45). However, ADDers often have concurrent Cluster B Personality Disorders (e.g. Borderline, Histrionic, Antisocial and Narcissistic Personality Disorders), often referred to as the Dramatic Cluster (46).

I used to believe that all of my feelings were real. And worth sharing. But feelings are always the result of our thoughts, and ADHD can cause an uncontrolled torrent of thoughts. The resulting emotional roller coaster wore me out. After I tried medication, my thoughts were far less chaotic. Once I began exercising and doing Yoga, there were brief moments of actual calm! Not quite Zen, but no longer a constant tornado of fears, concerns, opinions and upsets. Whew!

67.

Jumpin' Jack *Flash*

"I love extreme sports. Hang gliding. Parachuting. I snowboard and do double-diamond ski hills. I wouldn't say I am reckless because I get very focused. The world seems to go slower as I go faster. I have this amazing sense of control. Plus, I heal fast."

Meet the adrenaline junkie. Deliberately creating a crisis wakes up the ADHD brain. The fog clears. Now they can focus, intensely. Life becomes very simple in a crisis: You live or die. Black and white. No doubt there is calmness when decisions are reduced to basic choices.

By the way, adrenaline comes in many forms: passion, exhilaration, anger or anxiety. Other activities that create a sense of crisis are procrastinating, gambling, sleeping around or taking on far more than one person can sensibly handle.

I've said it before, I'll say it again, you want to find out if you have ADHD. Otherwise you are doing crazy things because it's the only time you feel alive. You're at the mercy of your biology and your life is not your own. Your hunger for 'brain juice' (Dopamine & Noradrenaline) is making your choices. Even if you're doing something healthy such as running marathons, an addiction to exercise is still an addiction. When I took on treatment, my brain got the 'juice' it lacked and I felt like I had choice. I had control. I was more 'me', not less.

68.

Secrets & *Lies*

"I like to stir things up. Share some gossip. Tell secrets. Blab. Create melodramas. I worry that I have this perverse need to see others in pain. Maybe because I always feel bad about myself."

Add a little mischief, a little melodrama and suddenly the ADDer is playing a fun game. They may gossip, lead people on, play people off each other and stir things up. They seem to draw some satisfaction in seeing people embarrassed or suffering. These games are dangerous, and stressful for others. In fact, this is actually a subtle form of bullying. Ironically, these ADDers were probably bullied as children. But it's time for the mind games to stop.

At some point I noticed that when I was feeling crappy about myself, I gossiped a lot. When I was on a roll, feeling good, I didn't. In fact, when other people gossiped I actually felt uncomfortable. When you feel good about yourself, you don't need to get your self-esteem at the expense of others. Or so I was told by this know-it-all jerk who is a complete… Sorry.

69.

Unpredictable *Volcano*

"I will drive miles out of my way to avoid slow traffic. When I get stuck in a lineup or any situation where I have to wait, I throw a hairy fit, embarrassing myself or worse... my family."

Pure impatience. The world is frustrating to the ADDer, especially when people do not see situations or conflicts from their point of view. On top of that is a constant feeling of urgency, even when the situation is not urgent. There is a certain narcissism in believing that the world should acknowledge their importance and get out of the way. But alas, it won't. Who is the ADDer really mad at? Themselves.

The lady ahead of me steps up to the ATM, sets her purse down and begins searching for her wallet. F*#%!! She's been waiting in line for five minutes, doing nothing, why didn't she look for her bank card then? Now she wastes my precious time! What a clueless, ignorant, self-absorbed cow!!... Ahem.

That was the old me. Now, I notice when my anger is rising and I pull out my smart phone. If my kids get a text message from me, it's because I'm waiting somewhere. I stay calm by taking action rather then being at the mercy of some clueless, hare-brained idiot who is wasting my... Really, I'm much calmer now. I swear.

70.

Zen? When?

"At work I'm thinking I should be with my husband and kids. When I'm with them, I'm fretting about work, or the gardening that needs doing, or my church group. If I meet with my church group, I feel guilty that I'm not with my family..."

 Everyone can become lost in thought; but having ADHD makes it worse. Worrying about things other than what they are doing right now is very common amongst ADDers. And no wonder. Their brain naturally jumps around. So they are rarely present.

For example, a patient told me, "Just once I would actually like to taste the dessert." She would have a craving and order some cake. But as she ate it, her mind would be off noodling about something else. She got all of the calories and none of the pleasure.

 In Buddhism they say, "Be here now." I was never here now. That constant sense of, 'This isn't it,' wore a bit thin after my first 50 years. A simple strategy I use now to be more present is 'No TV, books or distractions when I'm eating.' Simple right? It's actually incredibly difficult. But now I actually taste my food. (Bonus: I noticed that junk food actually tastes crappy. So I eat better.)

71.

Penal Brain

"A number of times I've been flirting with someone and it's gotten out of control. It's like I almost forget that I'm married. I haven't done anything, but I have to admit... I suspect I might."

 Breathing, thirst and hunger are basic to ones survival. Whereas many of our desires, such as sex or possessions, can be mistaken as needs, not wants. We confuse them as necessary for survival. The desire for sex can shut off the rational mind. Unfortunately, ADDers live in a constant survival mode, and this can lead to sexual addiction. Or an addiction to shopping. When we can transcend our primitive instincts, then we are truly free. Perhaps this is why all the major religions promote charity (giving without recognition) and sexual constraint (fighting ones primitive, impulsive urges).

 I must admit that being dragged to church did influence my morals. Then, as I got older, I became more spiritual. There was a desire to connect to a higher order, to Mother Earth, the Goddess, especially with the big hooters and the hot booty... Sorry, what was this about again?

72.

Die Working

"At work I'm Go, Go, Go! At home, I turn every leisure activity into a huge job, with deadlines and urgency. I know the stress is pushing my blood pressure up and it spoils things for my family. But knowing doesn't help."

ADDers feel as if they are always behind and that they are 'not good enough'. They spend their adult life trying to compensate for an inadequacy of childhood. Some call this ambition, and this striving for idealism can be good. Others become workaholics, feeling only fleeting pleasure from their successes; this is typical of the ADDer. Even on vacation they can't relax, so they'll pack in more and more activities. They're stuck on a treadmill that they can't get off or even slow down.

Ah yes, that avalanche of ideas that is both exhilarating and exhausting. Each new idea leads to a dozen more, each another commitment with more To-Do's, until I am overwhelmed. Luckily I discovered that vacations are not a frivolous waste of time; they allow me to recharge and be more productive. Balance. Hey, even the best hockey player has to spend time on the bench resting and recovering.

Chapter Seven

Disorders that Resemble, or Combine with ADHD

ADHD is challenging to diagnose because over 70% of cases involve a co-morbidity. That is, some other disorder that is directly related to having ADHD, or some other disorder that happens to be there at the same time.

In either case, the second disorder makes diagnosing even more tricky. One disorder may mask or blur the other.

It is likely that so much Adult ADHD goes undiagnosed because clinicians, unfamiliar with ADHD or the co-morbid conditions, will miss what's going on. Separating out the symptoms of one disorder from another can take time and patience.

The fact is, people with ADHD also suffer from higher rates of many other disorders. In this chapter we catalogue some of the most common co-morbidities.

73.

Blue Tunes

"All I remember growing up was the tone of adults constantly nagging me. Constant corrections and little digs that I couldn't escape or switch off. At some point I just gave up and stopped caring. By high school I suspect I was clinically depressed."

Learned helplessness. You may have heard of Seligman's experiment (47) where dogs were put in a closed room then given constant small shocks; eventually they gave up trying to escape. Even when offered a way out, the mentally exhausted dog would lay there, resigned to its fate.

The same thing can happen to an ADHD child. Each day they are stung by "Stop that!", "Don't do that!", "Cut it out!" There is no escape. No elusive door. We now know that a lifetime of high expressed emotion pushes one towards depression (48). Not surprisingly, mood disorders are a common co-morbidity for adult ADDers (49). Antidepressants may help with some symptoms, but they won't alleviate the core problems of their ADHD. Doctors who fail to ask, "How long has this been going on?" are far more likely to miss the ADHD and only diagnosis the Depression.

Many adults who have battled Depression take the Virtual Doctor test at TotallyADD.com and score off the charts for ADHD. Small wonder we have higher rates of Depression. When you keep screwing up simple things, things everyone else can do easily, it's depressing!

74.

I live in *O. B. City*

"Yes, obesity. I eat too much. I couldn't stop binging as a teenager. I still do it occasionally as an adult. There is a point of no return. After the fifth chip, that bag is as good as gone, and the fridge is next. I can't stop."

 ADDers are prone to Eating Disorders (50). Why? Possible reasons include: 1) Binging is connected to other impulsivity issues; 2) Sugary foods keep their revved engines running but they don't consider their metabolism slows in adulthood; 3) The craving may soothe anxiety; 4) ADDers habitually eat while watching TV or surfing the Net; 5) Poor time management and a low tolerance for frustration make fast foods a no-brainer.

While some of the medications for ADHD can cause weight loss in children, they usually don't do the same for adults. But, they may help control binging and purging (51)

 Personally, I'm at my perfect weight. I'm just way below my perfect height. I have devoured three-course meals without tasting a thing, because I'm watching TV and glancing through a book on ADHD. Now and then, I try to eat like I'm at a gourmet restaurant: no distractions, savoring each expensive bite. Bonus: I notice I'm full and stop eating before I'm stuffed and bloated. Which is never a great feeling anyway.

75.

Impending Doom

"I was a nervous kid and I'm still high strung. Sometimes it's just a general dread; fearful, doubting everything, when, in fact, things are fine. I compensate by preparing for any and every possible disaster. So then people figure I am a control freak."

ADDers have higher rates of Anxiety Disorders (52). All anxiety starts with two words, "What if…" A fear of the unknown. "What if I don't check the locks? Someone might break into the house." "What if I eat that grape? I will gain 14 pounds." "What if I talk in front of a crowd and make a fool of myself? I'll die from shame." What if? What if? What if? Anxiety results from seeing the world as unpredictable, dangerous and full of impending doom.

But could their anxiety come from the undiagnosed ADHD? Those with the Predominantly Inattentive Subtype may be at risk because as introverts they hold everything in. Whereas ADDers with the Predominantly Combined Subtype may try controlling their impulsive behavior by creating anxiety. They literally imagine disaster to stop themselves from doing risky things. Whatever the case, by adulthood, the anxiety can be as disabling as their ADHD.

No wonder undiagnosed ADHD leads to anxiety. I would agonize, "What if I completely screw up this huge, expensive television production?! I mean, I can't even trust myself to keep track of my cell phone! How can I possibly do this?"

76.

eroM daB sweN!

"I have a Learning Disorder. It's dyslexia. I keep reversing my letters. School was brutal. Now someone's suggesting I have ADHD? Please! I don't need MORE BAD NEWS."

The rates of dyslexia (reading problems that involve letter reversal) are much higher in people with ADHD. In fact, 40 to 60% of ADDers can have a concurrent Learning Disorder (LD) which, obviously, can cause additional problems (44).

An LD is a separate disorder, independent of ADHD. When they occur together, the attention difficulties of ADHD may make it harder to deal with the LD. Sometimes, because their ADHD is more obvious, a person's LD escapes notice. In adults the treatment for ADHD commonly fails because the LD is the bigger issue.

An LD requires a psychometric assessment by a registered psychologist. Unfortunately, it can be expensive even if you have insurance coverage.

The only upside of having a Learning Disorder is that there's far less stigma or dismissal than there is of ADHD. Plus many schools are willing to deal with it. It's the difference between being in the slow-learner class versus the behavioral class. Growing up, I was in the stay-after-class class.

77.

Beep, Whoop, *"#$&*!?!"*

"After starting treatment for ADHD, I developed tics. My mom claims the tics were there even before I took medication. In my teens they came back; tics, twitches, noises, and vocalizations. Plus I would get stuck in my thinking and I developed odd superstitions. Finally someone suggested it might be Tourette Syndrome."

 Seventy percent of people with Tourette Syndrome (TS) have ADHD (53). Are the tics and the ADHD independent? Likely not. Sometimes the tics are minor until the person begins active treatment for their ADHD. The treatment doesn't cause tics, it uncovers them (54). The ADHD part however is the more impairing component of TS and so are obsessive-compulsive symptoms. The person is usually not bothered by the tics unless they are being teased.

 I am fortunate to speak to many groups and recently I did a presentation for the Tourette Syndrome Foundation. These people are amazing and inspiring. In my talk I recalled that my Grade 2 teacher had a facial tic--when we pissed her off she would blink and twitch mercilessly. At the time, I thought she had an alien trapped inside, trying to break out of her. It's amazing what a 7-year-old imagines. Mind you, when I was 15, I had an English teacher who had a 'he' trying to break out of her. Eventually 'he' did... Sorry, I got off topic. Did I mention I have ADHD?

78.

Whirling Dervish

"I admit, I tend to be up and down and very emotional. If I were a car, I would be a Nitro Fueled Drag Racer: zero to 300 in seconds, then suddenly back to zero after I run out of gas. People have suggested that I am Bipolar or have a minor version called Bipolar II."

The symptoms of ADHD overlap Bipolar Disorder (previously called Manic-Depression) (45). Can ADHD and a Bipolar Disorder (BD) occur together? This is a very controversial question. Are some kids with ADHD actually BD in disguise? So far, it's unclear.

We do know that when we assess for BD, the symptoms should be cyclical. Also, they should not be related to a situational crisis; a reaction to a death or other major life event. Like ADHD, Bipolar tends to run in families. A psychiatric expert may be necessary to make the diagnosis.

BD and ADHD labels are an improvement over the much older diagnoses: "Possessed by Demons" or "A Witch." The generally prescribed treatment involved bloodletting or burning at the stake. As late as 1950, the prescribed treatment for Depression was a Prefrontal Lobotomy. In fact Dr. Egas Moniz won a Nobel Prize in 1949 for that procedure (55). Yikes! If your doctor suggests a Lobotomy, I would get a second opinion.

79.

Mr. *Spock*

"I was shy and quiet as a child. I'm still uncomfortable in big groups. I prefer one-on-one, or doing stuff by myself because I don't enjoy small talk and stuff like that. Actually, I'm happiest at work, where there are lots of people like me. I program computers in Silicon Valley."

This individual might have been diagnosed with Asperger's (a high functioning form of Autism) or an Anxiety Disorder (56). It may not be either of these. The Predominantly Inattentive Subtype of ADHD overlaps with both of these disorders due to the internalizing nature of the conditions. The treatments are really quite different so obtaining a reliable diagnosis is critical.

Did you know that Mr. Bean is used in England as a therapeutic tool to help kids understand Asperger's Syndrome? Mr. Spock and Data from Star Trek also resonate with Asperger folks. And now, there's Sheldon on The Big Bang Theory.

On the TotallyADD.com website we have Bill, the ADHD poster boy. Boy, do ADDers ever identify with him. Personally, I identify with Batman or Sponge Bob Square Pants, depending on how my day is going.

80.

Psychiatrist *Envy*

"My psychiatrist thinks she knows everything! Frankly, I know myself better than she ever will. She should be paying me to be her patient. I could teach her a few things. I should write a fascinating paper on my interaction with her. I'll do it later."

In my own studies of Personality Disorders (PD), 78% of ADDers have a co-morbid problem with a PD (46). They tend to divide based upon their temperament. Introverts are prone to more of the Cluster C Neurotic PD's. (i.e. They think too much.) Extroverts tend to have Cluster B Dramatic PD's. (i.e. They feel too much.) Unfortunately, a clinician may only detect the PD, which can be obvious and irritating; they miss the ADHD that precipitates it.

I've been diagnosed as a Narcissistic, Obsessive-Compulsive, Paranoid with a Passive-Aggressive Personality Disorder. By myself. The fact is, I know everything, and I know people are jealous of me so I undercut their value by making jokes about them. (Softly) Dr. J is actually a plumber.

Did you say something Rick?

No, no, carry on.

81.

Brain Freeze

"Several years ago I got hit playing hockey and was knocked unconscious. Afterwards my family noticed that I had trouble concentrating and getting stuff done. Finishing high school was tough, and my dream of becoming a hockey star was over. Now someone says I might have ADHD."

A head injury to the frontal lobes can look like ADHD. If the person actually had ADHD before the accident it may exaggerate the symptoms. An expert assessment is necessary. Can other things simulate ADHD? Yes. Congenital disorders and prenatal insults such as Fetal Alcohol Disorder (57) produce similar impairment. ADHD medications may help these problems, but the effectiveness is unpredictable.

One of the experts on TotallyADD.com is Dr. Derryck Smith, Professor and past Head of Psychiatry at the University of British Columbia. Neat guy. He became a leading authority on head injuries and ADHD after treating several patients who appeared to have ADHD, but had no family history of the disorder. Baffled, Derryck finally asked, "Have you ever had a brain injury?" Each one replied, "Yes." He was thunderstruck, "Why didn't you tell me before?" They all had the same answer, "You didn't ask." Now he always asks.

82.

Medically Manic

"A few years back I became really hyperactive. For no reason. People noticed that my eyes were popping out of my head. Despite not sleeping well, I had a tremendous amount of energy, in fact my heart was always pounding. Someone suggested ADHD and recommended I ask for meds. Not a good idea, it turns out."

 This is hyperthyroidism (58). It looks very similar to ADHD. The thyroid gland (located where the Adam's Apple lies) is producing too much hormone and that makes the person hyperactive. This is a medical condition that is detected by blood tests and it can be treated. This person should not be given an ADHD medication as it might worsen their symptoms.

 Scary stuff. While a Psychologist can diagnosis ADHD, they can't rule out any medical abnormalities that merely look like it. That's why you want to see a Physician first. Now, before all the Psychologists start sending me hate mail, I want to acknowledge that they can do plenty that MDs can't, such as testing for Learning Disorders. In fact, I think that all the medical disciplines and specialties should just work together and get along. Especially proctologists. We do not want to make them angry.

83.

Blind as a Bat

"I sat in the front seat of the class, but still struggled to keep up. I also had headaches and couldn't concentrate. Someone suggested ADHD. Luckily, my driving instructor noticed that I squinted as I drove. She asked, 'Do you need glasses?' Apparently, all these years I did."

It is so important to have hearing and vision tested. If a student can't see or hear properly, they become inattentive… they get restless… "Aha! ADHD!" You would think that this would be diagnosed in childhood but some individuals find a way to reach adulthood without their vision or hearing problem being noticed. The lesson is: Not everyone walking into the doctor's office with an attention problem has ADHD!

This reminds me of Dr. Annick Vincent's ADHD book, My Brain Needs Glasses (59). Some folks' eyes have trouble focusing, so do some folks' brains. And of course innumerable ADDers have told us that treatment is, "Like being near-sighted and finally putting on glasses. Suddenly everything comes into focus."

For some reason tight underwear makes my brain focus. Probably a side effect from forcing all that extra blood to my head. Is there a reliable study or scientific paper or research initiative that can explain this?

Uh, no.

84.

Scrambled Eggs

"Drugs? Well, I smoked cigarettes when I was 11, then progressed to mushrooms, glue and then weed. Cocaine was a waste; it made me calm. As an adult, I have stopped most everything except cigarettes and pot. And alcohol is more a social thing."

ADDers tend to self-medicate once they find something that helps lower the 'noise'. And yes, marijuana will do that. It will also strip the person of their motivation and drive (60). Beyond the effect on brain chemistry, there can be a strong social pressure to do drugs because ADDers may be desperate to fit in. The good news is, if we treat the ADHD then the addiction can be helped (58). I have worked with long-standing addicts who stopped using cocaine once their ADHD was properly treated. Thirty years of cocaine destruction, stopped, voluntarily. Wow!

I know so many creative people who self-medicate with illicit drugs. Hey, I don't particularly trust big pharmaceutical companies either... but drug dealers? Not at all.

Save your money and your sinuses.

Chapter Eight

Familiar Frustrations of ADHD Adults

By now you've guessed it; ADDers have to cope with a world that was meant for that narrow definition of 'normal' people. Or as ADDers tend to refer to them, The Boring Majority.

This chapter describes some of the things that make it hard for the ADDer to get through the day. We also provide some helpful solutions, here and at TotallyADD.com

If you are new to the world of ADHD, continue to ride your learning curve. There is a lot that is worth knowing; and a lot of misinformation to sort through. If you have been at this for a while, the strategies and solutions we offer may be skills you have already developed. Some may serve as a timely reminder.

85.

Contract *Killer*

"I'm not stupid but paper makes me feel like I am. I've signed mortgages, bank loans, tax forms, certificates and car leases without reading any of the fine print. Or the big print. It was just too much."

Oh man, this is familiar. I know I'm supposed to carefully read contracts, but hey, as long as it's in English, I will sign anything. And not just financial paperwork. Instructions and warranties would be glanced at, then filed under my special system known as PILES (Paper In Lumps Everywhere Someplace). When something broke, locating the warranty was impossible, so I would have to buy a new one.

Paperwork requires mental energy, focus and diligence. The ADDer can't really see the reward. Things like, "Having my paperwork all caught up, well organized and paid on time so I avoid late fees and have extra money in my pocket? That seems so far in the future that it's borderline theoretical."

Plus, the ADDer has no faith that if they ever did get caught up it would stay that way. Rather than wait for another crisis to spur them to action they must create a structure. A good first step is to buy a small accordion file and put all of the most important paperwork in it. All together, in one place that's easy to find.

86.

Sibling *Schism*

"I believe my parents favored my siblings, though they would never admit it. My brothers and sisters claim that I got all the attention. Sorry, being yelled at isn't attention, is it? I was the Black Sheep, the scapegoat for everyone else's problems."

This person's belief may in fact be true. Why? ADDers may subconsciously wish they didn't have siblings so they could have their parents' undivided attention. When the parents have another child, the ADDer wonders, "What, I wasn't good enough?"

Inevitably, they feel they are being compared to their siblings and slowly they take on the victim stance: "Nobody loves me." However, when parents recall the past they say, "He got 90% of the attention in the family and it was never enough." Attention, yes. But, it may have been negative attention. Now, as an adult, the ADDer still believes they're doomed to failure. Ironically, when an ADDer takes on treatment and starts to be productive, they may face resistance from a family that is stuck in an unhealthy, but familiar dynamic where the ADDer remains the scapegoat.

As a C+ student sandwiched between the two straight A brothers, I felt like I slipped between the cracks. (Notice it's not how it was, it's what I felt.) It was a situation I encouraged; hiding out was preferable to being reminded about my mediocre marks. Now that I know that it was the ADD that had me tuned out in school, I've stopped resenting my brothers. In fact, I've stopped letting the air out of their tires.

87.

Nap-o-*philia*

"I tire easily. Without frequent breaks my productivity tanks. Every task starts out looking like a mountain to me, even paying a simple bill. I get tired just thinking about it. The weird thing is, I'm really good at routine physical jobs."

The ADDer's brain is like a blast furnace. It requires a huge amount of fuel because it is processing so much extra information; naturally mental exhaustion is common. There may not be enough energy left over to do physical tasks. So, the person appears to be unmotivated or almost comatose. Ironically, when the work is primarily physical, it seems to make their brain relax. Doing manual labor is a breeze. More importantly, we know that keeping physically active actually makes the brain work better. So they might, for example, do some push ups before taking on their tax paperwork.

My brain is either half-asleep or on full Def Con 4 Alert at which point I am on, in the zone, and going full tilt boogie until I crash. Hey, I'm a sprinter. My wife can't understand how I can nap; out like a light, then snorting myself awake 20 minutes later with tons of mental energy. I wish I had the cats' freedom to nap whenever and wherever. And possibly the ability to clean myself like cats do. There I go again, TMI.

88.

Holy *Shirt!*

"I can be kind of fussy or finicky. Like snipping off the tags from the collar of every one of my blouses because they drive me crazy. Years ago when I finally found a pair of socks that didn't bother me, I went back and bought ten pairs. Now they're worn out and I wish I'd bought twenty."

ADDers seem to be hypersensitive to their environment. For example, a college student listens to music to help them study. But if someone else is playing music, even if it's at a lower volume, they find it distracting. Even infuriating. When an ADDer asks for a hug, they love it. But touch them unexpectedly and they may cringe.

An ADDer who is conscious of the smells, tastes, sights, sounds and touch sensations in their environment, and can adjust and control them, has a better chance of focusing on what they need to.

If I am concentrating on something—driving, writing or following an interesting football play—and my wife touches me, especially lightly, it's annoying. Not as bad as fingernails on a chalkboard; more like, when someone starts talking during a movie. Mostly I encourage touching. Nudge nudge, wink wink. Just not while I'm driving.

89.

Timed Trouble

"I sit down to watch TV for a minute and the whole evening zips by, but when I run on our treadmill, time suddenly slows down and 15 seconds takes a week. It's like time is thumbing its nose at me in some kind of cruel joke."

ADDers have distorted time perception (61). Sometimes they zoom through a task only to discover they've made numerous little mistakes. At other times they zone out, unaware of how much time has actually passed, and spend far too much time on irrelevant details.

Very few of my patients wear watches or check the time on their cell phones. Despite dreading deadlines they rely on them to get anything done. Always at the last minute. They resist using agendas despite knowing it would improve their work productivity and, yes, give them more leisure time.

Agendas? Those were for 'boring people', who had to submit to 'the system'. Planning? That felt like buckling under, becoming a cog in the system. Me? I wanted to be spontaneous. Free! Alas, I confused a dislike for being 'controlled by others' with being 'on top of things and in control'. When I discovered that an agenda lowers stress, everything shifted. This was about the same time I figured out that my parents were no longer in charge of me. I was 48 at the time.

90.

Night *Hawk*

"I am most productive between 1:00 and 4:00 AM, though I can't get up until noon. In College I missed all my morning lectures. To get my internal clock working right I should move to another time zone. Or become a vampire."

ADDers often have difficulty falling asleep at night and/or waking up in the morning. They may also suffer from daytime fatigue, restless sleep, and frequent waking through the night (62). There could be many reasons for this: 1) There is less distraction in the calm of the night so they prefer to work then; 2) Their brain's sleep efficiency may be affected by passively stimulating activity (e.g. light from the TV or computer); 3) There is a link between low exposure to sunlight in the winter disrupting sleep and causing mood changes (63). 4) They procrastinate so much they have to work late to get things finished.

Whatever the reasons, a lack of sleep directly affects their mental and physical health. The ADDer must address this problem, because sleep is crucial to being able to pay attention (64).

I was drawn to show business because my body clock seemed to be 6 hours behind everyone else's. The thought of performing in the evening, staying up late, and having breakfast at noon? Awesome! When I learned that TV shows start production at 7:00 in the morning, I was horrified. Coffee. More coffee!

91.

Elusive Answer

"All I ever hear is, 'Don't do that!', but no one ever explains what I'm actually supposed to do. Apparently, the right choice is obvious to everyone but me. Left to figure it out, I inevitably guess wrong. Then someone is right there explaining how I screwed up yet again."

 When someone does something irritating we tend to snap, "Stop that", "Don't do that", or "No". It turns out that ADDers really hate these negative messages. To the ADDer, "No" evokes more than just disappointment over not getting what they want; it may actually bring up feelings of rejection and abandonment.

Try reframing the message as a positive. For example, "If you don't empty the dishwasher, you can't go watch the game with your buddies." emphasizes the "don't-can't" words. Here's the positive reframe, "After you do the dishes, I want you to go enjoy yourself with your buddies." The "do-want" feels so much better. ADDers thrive with clear, simple and positive communication.

 No kidding. Mom would holler, "Change your underwear or you can't go out!" so I would change into the pair I wore yesterday. I alternated. Well apparently that wasn't good. If only she'd been clearer, "Put on fresh underwear every day," perhaps I would have finally understood. Perhaps. Hey, I have ADHD, but I'm also a guy.

92.
Unsolvable *Solved*

"I can problem solve anything. Too bad 'Brain Stormer' is not an actual job because I'd be rich. Even if I don't know much about whatever problem I am looking at, I have the ability to find a solution."

Years ago I wrote and hosted Prisoners of Gravity, a TV series about comic books, fantasy, horror and science fiction. I was by no means an expert, but I talked to people who were, the self-described nerds, before starting the script. Afterwards they'd exclaim, "Yes, that's it exactly! I never thought of it that way." My friend Mark, the brain behind the series, told me the screenwriter for the 2009 Watchmen movie told him that he didn't fully understand the original comic book until he saw a rerun of our 'Watchmen' episode from 1993. Uh, do I get residuals? Profits? A handshake?

ADDers can be 'big picture' thinkers; think of Richard Branson. It's been said ADDers see the forest but not the trees. They think outside the box and that makes them very effective problem solvers. They can be inventive and creative.

Alas, despite this intuitive understanding of the world they may be poor at self-observation.

93.

Thirty Hour *Day*

"If I'm practicing my guitar, or doing something I like, I lose track of time and hours slip away. Then I'll snap out of it, realize I was supposed to be doing something urgent, and now it's a mad scramble to get caught up. There are never enough hours in the day."

ADDers have uneven focusing. For some things they are laser focused. Relentless. Unstoppable. Meanwhile, other more urgent tasks are avoided or fall by the wayside. No wonder their To-Do List seems inexhaustible. Time zips by and the ADDer feels ever more behind.

The key is to prioritize and that means making sure that the things that are important (the things that the ADDer is most avoiding) are done first. Then the rest of the day seems so much easier. Even better, wake up early, do the hard thing, and by the time the rest of the world is waking up, you are sipping coffee, proud of yourself.

At one point I was writing and acting for two different TV series at the same time, and also directing one of them. Oh, and doing some radio stuff in my spare time. Super focused and very productive. Yet I spent almost no time with my family, the very people I was trying to provide for. A perfect example of not prioritizing what mattered. My kids grew up and I missed it. I think they grew up. I should check and find out. One of them is named Julia or something.

94.

Shock or *Awe*

"Apparently I irritate people. For example I was told my laugh is loud so people don't sit next to me. I move a lot in the theatre seats and then people shush me. I'm minding my own business, explaining what's wrong with the movie while eating all my popcorn, and people are glaring at me. What's their problem?"

ADDers have a hard time self-regulating. They may not appreciate how loudly they talk, or how much their arms flail around in conversations, or how their silliness can be annoying. Sometimes the ADDer interprets feedback as malicious criticism and they overreact to helpful suggestions. So, when dealing with ADDers it is important to be nurturing. Start with what went right, what's working, what are their strengths. Acknowledge their good intentions. Then offer the suggestion or change.

OK, I can be silly. But look where it got me! Admittedly, it can wear a bit thin. Or so my wife has suggested. But I think people are jealous of my youthful vitality. I would rebut those who suggest I'm immature, with, "You stink, Poopy-faces! Nyah, Nyah!" Ha ha! I win!

95.

No *Noise* Abatement

"If the TV is on, even softly, and my husband says something from the kitchen, I'll miss it, and he'll have to repeat it. Twenty seconds later, when he says something else, I have to ask him to repeat that too. Doesn't he understand the TV is on?"

The human brain expends a lot of energy filtering out the irrelevant stuff and deciding what to focus on. The ADDer is not good at this. Their filtering is wildly uneven. If there are two people talking, they may be able to follow both, or neither. Usually they miss what was said. A simple strategy for the ADDer is to face the speaker and focus on their mouth, almost like lip-reading.

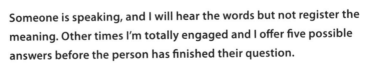

Someone is speaking, and I will hear the words but not register the meaning. Other times I'm totally engaged and I offer five possible answers before the person has finished their question.

My wife will think I'm not listening because I'm not looking at her and busy doing something else. I'll snap, "I heard you. We are leaving for the party in ten minutes." Of course, ten minutes later, I'm out in the backyard spreading compost, oblivious, and my wife is waiting by the front door in her party dress. Then it's her turn to snap.

96.

Conspiracy Theory!

"Sometimes I feel like everyone is out to hurt me. Or keep me down. I was bullied as a kid, then denigrated as an adolescent and humiliated as an adult. It's like there is this big secret to having a good life, that everyone knows except me."

There is no conspiracy. ADDers have an interpersonal awkwardness which makes them easy targets and that leads to all sorts of defensive reactions. Holding on to ones self-esteem becomes their biggest challenge. It's important because self-esteem assures resiliency, and with it the ADDer can become immune to life's slings and arrows. One strategy is to lighten up and develop an ability to laugh at oneself. Humour is a powerful protective shield. And self-deprecating humour is the best kind of all.

I used to think that I was targeted because I was an outsider, weird, or, heaven forbid... DIFFERENT! My self-esteem suffered until I realized that being different was not a bad thing. Non-conformity actually saved me. Forget trying to fit in, or being like everyone else. I am a funny, eccentric, goofball and I am okay with that. And of course, being one of the world's greatest studs also helps my self-esteem.

Chapter Nine

Familiar Complaints of the ADDer's Family

At our workshops we meet many adults who have recently received a proper ADHD diagnosis. They talk about the emotional roller coaster. One minute it's euphoria, relief, "Finally my life makes sense!" The next moment rage, "Why didn't anyone notice?" The next, regret and sadness, "If only I'd known sooner..."

Then someone sneers at them, "Nonsense. We all forget stuff! ADHD isn't real." They are left feeling mortified and perhaps even doubtful. It's easy for skeptics to dismiss ADHD because it is not obvious, unlike say, having a broken leg.

While the ADDer rides a roller coaster, so do those around them. Often well before the diagnosis. As the years pass, family, friends and colleagues may become as frustrated and confused as the person who has ADHD.

This chapter touches on those emotionally charged issues that families complain about to the ADDer. This is their point of view; it may be enlightening for the ADDer to hear what other people think. It may also give some insight into what needs to change.

97.

Mr. *Monologue*

Your loved ones say, "He dominates conversations. If anyone else talks, he gets louder. And every conversation somehow gets turned to a topic he finds interesting."

ADDers don't mean to come across as narcissistic Know-It-All's. Yet somehow the conversation always seems to shift so it is about them. It's not so bad if they are good storytellers, but this habit of not letting people express their views leaves others feeling dismissed and devalued. Eventually people see the ADDer as obnoxious and self-centered.

Listening is an important attribute. But try telling that to an ADDer!

My brother watched a movie, thinking, "I swear I've seen this, but it's not how I remember it." Then he realized he hadn't seen it; I had, and then told him all about it. The whole film! He said my version was way more entertaining. So clearly I tell good stories. Whether people want me to or not. There's the rub. I would talk, talk, talk, never thinking to listen.

Now I ask questions. Turns out other people have great stories too. The danger is I stop listening, waiting for a chance to tell my 'even better' story. In fact, one time, you wouldn't believe what happened... Sorry.

98.

Me, Me, *Me!*...

Those close to you complain, "It's always about you. It's always about how bad you feel or what I haven't done to help you. It's all, "Woe is me." Or "It's not fair." I am not your mother. Suck it up and take it like a man."

Why don't ADDers take responsibility for their actions? It may be because: 1) They have to defend their low self-esteem by deflecting blame; 2) They messed up because they weren't listening carefully to instructions; 3) They have a tendency to test people's loyalty by pushing their buttons; 4) They simply do not see someone else's point of view; or 5) They act childishly when they feel dominated by people in authority.

ADDers need to hear positives first to build up their self-esteem. That allows them to drop their defensiveness. Then one can offer them solution-focused suggestions.

Having to admit to mistakes takes courage. It's just easier to blame others because; after all, the world is full of dough-headed morons!

 Oh yes, and 6) They often test those around them by dismissing their advice or making them feel unappreciated.

 Sure, yeah, whatever **You're the big-shot expert with the fancy degrees.**

 OK, Rick, I know this is challenging, and you are a great guy... but, wanna take it outside, you little runt? Ahem. Sorry, lost it there.

99.

King of the Castle!

Others complain, "He's so competitive at board games, arguing over the rules and spoiling the fun. Sometimes he gets so loud it's uncomfortable. And worse, if someone else wins, there is a big scene and he pouts."

This ADDer has a need to dominate and win. It is as if their survival instinct has been awoken. I always suggest that the spouse/partner/sibling create a cue system with the ADDer ahead of time. A typical signal may be a rub of an eyebrow or a hand placed over their heart. The message is, "Something is wrong, adjust yourself".

Support, but never publicly embarrass, the ADDer.

When I caught myself trying to beat my adolescent daughter at Monopoly, I knew something was wrong. Now my wife signals me when I am being overly competitive. (Or not listening. Or chewing too loudly. Or have a nose hair hanging out.) For 'Not Listening' she casually tugs her ear. I'm usually embarrassed and then miffed at her... until I remember she's got my best interest at heart. (Dammit.)

100.

ADDer *Knows* Better

A loved one complains, "She doesn't care about my opinion. She dismisses my advice, claiming I am too negative. She refuses to admit there might be a problem and can barely conceal her disdain. Eventually she just tunes me out."

Loved ones of an ADDer must learn to keep quiet. This is very challenging. After all, the parent or spouse can see the ADDer is headed straight for disaster; why wouldn't they warn them? They're only trying to help. But giving unsolicited advice comes across as, "I don't trust you."

If someone would correct me, even if they knew more than I did, I'd have to prove I was right. Shields up! Defenses on! Attack!

ADDers often know a lot. But there's a big difference between being knowledgeable, and being a "Know-It-All." And… Uh… I have no idea what it is.

101.

The *Latest* Brain Fad!

Family members state, "She's always blaming her miserable life on some disorder. First it was Anxiety. Then Dyslexia. Then Depression. Now it's ADHD?! And apparently it's our fault because we're her parents and we didn't spot it. Spare us!"

The vast majority of psychiatrists don't know what ADHD is, or worse, may see it as some sort of character flaw.

But even after the ADDer manages to obtain a proper diagnosis, their family may dismiss it. Why? ADDers have a history of excuses, explanations and justifications. Eventually, the excuses don't even seem believable. To others it sounds like 'the boy who cried wolf.' So when the ADDer is finally diagnosed, their families tend to assume they're just avoiding responsibility with yet another excuse.

I came up with one explanation after another for what was 'wrong' with me; when you don't know what's going on, you can be very inventive. But after I had a proper diagnosis my friends and family were still skeptical. Even now the most hostile dismissals come from people who look to me like they have ADHD.

102.

*Pi*gheaded

Your loved ones complain, "It took him four tries to assemble a simple Ikea cabinet. There were instructions, but, oh no, he knew better. Of course, he scratched the veneer and had two screws left over. No wonder it wobbles."

ADDers often: 1) Think instructions and routines are for stupid people; 2) Hate being told what to do, because they've had a lifetime of scolding and nagging; 3) Don't do well with details because it takes a lot of mental effort; 4) Enjoy figuring things out, and don't want to have a blueprint and 5) Believe that they have good problem solving skills. The difficulty with their adventurous attitude is that when they start down a pathway they can end up taking the long way, with endless detours and backpedaling.

Yeah, I'd figure, "What's all the fuss about? The manufacturers always put a few extra screws in the package. Besides, I assembled the last three pieces of furniture just fine. And I put that lawnmower together no problem. So there!" Defensive? Me?! Defensive?!

103.

*Lazy*bones

A parent laments, "She took forever to do things. Homework was just painful; always late. Even as an adult she struggles over simple tasks because she is distracted. If there's something important that needs doing, I don't even ask, I just do it myself."

It's easy to mistake a failure to deliver for laziness. Ironically, to quote author Kate Kelly told us, "ADDers are working their hearts out, just to get through the day." There is no lack of effort, it's just squandered by doing things in an unstructured and an uncoordinated fashion. When tasks take a long time to complete the ADDer becomes sidetracked, then overwhelmed and finally quits.

The patio furniture needs washing because we're having a party. But being Mr. Helpful, I also water the flowers, help a neighbor fix his chain saw, repair two bikes and reorganize the entire tool shed. The furniture gets washed, barely in time. Then I remember I was also supposed to rake the leaves, wash the back steps and refill the barbecue tanks. Panic time!

Now I regularly stop and ask, "Is this what I'm supposed to be doing?" It's amazing how often the answer is "Nope."

104.

Mr. *Nosey*

People will complain, "She butts in on conversations, or offers her opinion even though no one asked for it. Even with people she's just met she'll start offering advice on personal problems. She means well but sometimes she comes across as intrusive, or meddling."

ADDers are natural rescuers. They enjoy the validation that comes from helping others. They crave praise so much that they leave their own messes unattended. Their house may be in shambles but if a neighbor needs their deck built, the ADDer is there, helping out.

Yes, they may intrude upon people's personal lives in the belief that they are being useful, but at what point does it become a nuisance? Naturally the ADDer may not be appreciated for their conscientious effort. And if people suggest that 'This really doesn't concern you," they feel insulted. Suddenly they are 'the Martyr'.

I helped our neighbors transform a huge pile of stones into a beautiful patio, and I pointed out all the things they were doing inefficiently, demonstrated the best way to use the tools and as a bonus, explained why their patio design wouldn't work for parties. Eventually they saw it my way. Funny, they never invited me to their patio parties. Jerks!

105.

Blame Shifter

Colleagues say, "It's never her fault. Rather than apologize, she'll lie or justify. I hate that."

To be able to take blame or shoulder responsibility a person needs strong, healthy self-esteem; something many ADDers lack. That's why they can be hyper-sensitive to criticism and immediately feel rejected. The solution? They need to know that the other person loves them. Without this safety zone ADDers have a natural predilection to defend themselves and/or to deflect responsibility to others.

How often have I said, "I want to take responsibility, but other people won't let me!" (Ahem.)

When I get defensive my wife calls me "Justin". As in Justin-the-Justifier. It's automatic; like holding up my arm to prevent being hit.

When I manage to avoid going into my defensive shell it is much easier to apologize for transgressions and take responsibility for screw-ups. Hey, we all make them. Especially since we are surrounded by idiots! (Sorry! That was Justin.)

106.

Fashions From *Another Planet*

Friends say, "She is oblivious to how she comes across; like with her wardrobe choices. She buys very interesting clothing items, really odd, quirky things, then she wears them all at once and looks like an explosion in a fabric store!"

Many of my patients work in creative fields: TV, Media, Fashion or Advertising. In fact, a colleague at U.C.L.A. suggested, "They should take down the HOLLYWOOD sign and put up ADHD CITY!

So some ADDers are acutely fashion savvy and become trendsetters. But others are the opposite. When they look in the mirror it may not click that their socks are different colors, or that their shirt is buttoned wrong, and hey, how many times does their fly have to be at half mast?

Or it may be that general ADHD extremism. ADDers can be rebels, "If I want to wear nine kinds of plaid I will." When worn-out, cut-up jeans became fashionable, you just know that had to be an ADDer's idea.

Four words: "My wife dresses me."

107.

Sibling *Rivalry*

Your siblings recall, "When we went on car trips he would get bored, tease us, pinch, poke, grab… until we'd explode. And he was grinning, like it was fun. Eventually Mom would turn around and smack him one. If he didn't stop Dad would stop the car and really let him have it."

ADDers can be pests. What's the recipe? Combine one part impulsiveness (an ADHD kid is more likely to hit first and think about the consequences later) with one part goofiness (ADDers sometimes can't tell what is silly vs. funny) and add a dash of alpha male competitiveness (to get their parents' undivided attention) and a generous helping of a smart-mouthed chatter, stir for 5 hours in a locked car, and there you have it: Hell. It takes less than 5 hours if the Dad is also ADHD and sets the example of what a kid should not do.

I think my father appreciated my, uh, 'uniqueness' and nurtured my sense of humor. (Which was just like his.) However, there is a difference between genuinely funny and annoyingly goofy. I am not clear what that difference is but, I am clear that as a comedian, being funny pays the bills.

But you're always late paying your bills.

Funny, eh?

108.

Where's *Mommy?*

Your sister says, "ADHD? Bull! She just takes on way too much. She has work, her church group, the soccer league, theatre group, kids... If I had her schedule, I'd look like I have Attention Deficit Whatever! No one could follow through on everything she promises."

 There could be many reasons why ADDers get into overwhelm: 1) They often take longer to do things. So when they extend themselves, they get bogged down faster and start to drown. 2) They feel compelled to say yes to combat rejection. "Now, you will like me." 3) ADDers need pressure to keep their brain activated; over-committing is a coping strategy; 4) ADDers get bored easily and taking on new tasks, whether or not the others are finished, is energizing.

Naturally, they become workaholics. Work is a drug. They can't seem to stop. When they do manage to stop, it's a struggle to restart. They are either very on or very off.

 For a long time I couldn't imagine a day without work. Now, I'm learning to seek balance. I'm not there yet, but work is no longer all-consuming. As for retirement, are you kidding? Lounging in an old age home discussing bowel movements with other geezers? With my tendency to try to outdo everyone else that could become dangerously competitive. Rather than ever retire, I'll simply pursue new interests.

Chapter Ten

How ADHD Impacts Work and Finances

In this chapter we explore common problems that ADDers encounter at work and while managing their finances.

It's well understood that ADHD impacts a child's development, socially and academically. But the impairment doesn't end with childhood. School was disheartening, but now you are thrust out into the real world; the world of responsibility, accountability and financial obligations. The stakes keep going up, and the structures of youth—parents and teachers—are no longer there to keep you on track. Luckily, you're an adult now, with insight and more self-awareness.

Some of the symptoms in previous chapters will reappear here in the context of work. You may notice similarities between some of the childhood impairments and those of adults. Hey, schoolwork is work.

109.

The *Hurricane* Filing System

"My paperwork is a mess. I kind of know where everything is, and what is in each large pile, unless a pile topples onto the floor. I do waste time moving stacks of paper around. I could probably throw most of this stuff out, but where do I start? Locating my garbage pail, I guess."

Paper is kryptonite to the ADDer. They move paper around rather than handle it or toss it. "What if I need it?" they muse. There are only two things in life that are not replaceable: your family photos & videos and the last seven years of tax receipts. Everything else is replaceable. It is certainly insurable. ADDers must free themselves from the endless clutter of stuff that they never use and let it go.

Gather and toss. LUMP & DUMP. That's another ADD mantra.

Lump and Dump? Sounds dirty.

Sometimes I suspect my paperwork is breeding and multiplying; conspiring to bury me alive. Death by a thousand paper cuts. Why do I still have the instructions for my childhood slot car set, a flyer from 8 Track of the Month Club, leg-hair removal coupons, hundreds of photos of people I dislike and 240 magazine articles on de-cluttering? After realizing that everything I'll ever need is on the Internet somewhere, I've become diligent about tossing paper.

110.

Where's the *Money?*

"I never seem to have money. One reason is that I haven't sent in my invoices for the past eight months."

ADDers don't value themselves and often under-charge for fear they will be rejected. Worse, they may never submit invoices to be paid. They rely on quick fixes like credit cards so that their VISA card is paying off their MasterCard. They ask family for loans. They bother friends or colleagues for money. Quick investments. They become Ponzi prey. Falling for online scams. ADDers fail with money. Notoriously. In our society, that adds a lot of emotional baggage.

Some people develop a huge lump in their body but never see a doctor because they don't want to know if it's bad news. For me, that lump is my wallet. Money scares me. Usually I have no idea if I am rich or bankrupt. Thank goodness my wife is good with money. Or so she claims. Hmm. Maybe she's robbing me blind! Never mind, I don't want to know.

111.

The *Price* of Freedom

"To most people the Water Works and Electric Company are just squares on a Monopoly Game. But I actually know where the real utilities are in my town because I've I had to drive to their offices with a certified check so they wouldn't cut off my power."

ADDers keep getting dinged with extra interest charges on their taxes or credit cards because they are perpetually late. How many times must they worry that the house might burn down before the late payment arrives at the insurance company? How many times must their credit score bottom out because they missed the "minimum payment option"? How many times do they have to dodge collection agencies over some payment that was "lost in the mail"? It's illogical, but they pay these extra penalties and continue to procrastinate.

This is painfully familiar for me. The worst part is, I had the money, but I was 'too busy' to stop at the bank and move it over. Busy working to make more money.

The answer? Hire a bookkeeper and set up automatic payments. The savings in late fees, and wear and tear on your nerves, will be enormous. Believe me.

112.

Dilbert's™ *Boss*

"I always end up working for brainless idiots. Until they fire me. They don't appreciate that I can see things they can't. I have big ideas but they are stuck on small mistakes and nit-picking details. They don't trust that I have the smarts to smooth over problems as we go."

Positive mentorship is a critical component to the success of the ADDers in their workplace. If the ADDer admires and feels nurtured by their boss they will have tremendous loyalty. In these circumstances, the ADDer will rise to challenges, outperforming others. A respected mentor is the key!

The opposite is also true. A boss who criticizes and does not show leadership will be rejected through passive resistance. Inevitably, the ADDer will be fired and, just as inevitably, they will be baffled, asking, "What did I do wrong, and why didn't anyone tell me?"

I would submit scripts, and when they came back, rewritten, I'd smolder, "Why did they remove that joke!? Idiots!" What I wouldn't acknowledge was that they had cut out nine other jokes that were kind of lame. I'd fixate on the one that I thought was funny. Great use of energy, right? The joke was on me. And I didn't get it.

113.

Underpaid for *Underachieving*

"I feel lucky to have this job, because I'm so incompetent. I plan to stay at this level because I know I can handle it. The trick is to not be noticed; I have amazing ways of being invisible or looking busy. I work in more than one place so no one really knows where I am or what I do.

ADDers sometimes underestimate their value and undercut their self worth. Growing up feeling rejected makes one gun shy. They avoid conflict situations, but flying under the radar is tricky. It takes a certain talent; one that many ADDer's master. But the irony is that the harder they try to be invisible the more pain they suffer because it reinforces the feeling that they aren't "good enough".

Failures were a mystery. "What did I do wrong?" Same with successes. "What did I do right?" So I had no confidence that I could reproduce the same results. I was just glad to get paid. Understanding my ADHD exposed the hidden saboteur! Now I can avoid the failures and actually enjoy my successes. Wow!

114.

Boston *Terrier*

"I need a lot more supervision, guidance and feedback. My supervisor says he has to micromanage me. I resent being put on a leash, but I have to admit, it keeps me on track."

Despite being creative, insightful and energetic, the ADDer can be like a Boston Terrier straining at the leash to go. They can't slow down and since asking for help is not easy, they rush into things, inevitably making mistakes.

Some solutions: 1) Clearly understand the expectations at work; 2) Have a boss who makes them accountable, but provides a sense of positive guidance and 3) Have the boss breakdown big tasks into smaller steps. Chunk them up.

I've also found that if things are not moving fast enough I am prone to mistakes. My first summer job was at the Department of Health, sorting the oversized plastic and metal containers that doctor's used to ship the bottles of urine and feces samples to labs. But the glamour wore off after a week. Then I discovered I could read a book while I sorted and never make a mistake. But my boss didn't understand how I could do two things at once, and told me to stop reading and slow down. Having to go slowly drove me crazy and I asked for a transfer. They sent me upstairs to clean the cages of the lab rats. That was interesting.

115.

Day Late, *Dollar Short*

"I'm always late with everything. My work is great. Even groundbreaking. But I have to admit it's usually delivered after the deadline. And yeah, it's full of small mistakes, but so what."

Why are ADDers always late? Perhaps it's because: 1) They take on too much; 2) They have trouble with time management; 3) They are so used to procrastination that last minute deadlines seem natural; 4) They have poor delegating ability or 5) They may have a deficit of sequencing skill – they can't seem to break things down into logical steps.

Another ADHD mantra: DELIVER.

Every project starts out full of promise. My energy is boundless. I'm pounding it out. It's incredible. Then, at some point I fade a bit, dealing with endless details, or sidetracked by a problem… Completing that last 10% is murder. I feel like I am pedaling a bike that is stuck in low gear. Getting the diagnosis gave me access to all the gears. Until then life was giving me the gears. (Wow, that's clever. I need a nap now.)

116.

Know-It-All Attitude

My boss claims, "When he started here he had some great ideas. We still use them. But would I hire him again? Nope. I don't need the ulcer. Mr. Know-It-All never followed the rules; he said they were outdated. He was never a team player. Smart guy, lousy people skills."

The ADDer makes a great first impression, gets a foot in the door and then the stubbornness and deflecting responsibility starts. They have difficulty listening or following rules.

They are given a task. It doesn't sound hard, so for the first 29 days of the month, they do nothing. Then on the last day they bang it out in a mad scramble. Yet again. They actually deliver something good, but full of small mistakes. "I'll fix those." Imagine the chagrin of their colleagues. "He goofs off all month, and still beats me in sales!" But it's a dangerous game – sometimes the squeaky wheel gets replaced.

The problem isn't when I suspect that I know better than everyone else. It's when I know that I know better. That's for certain. Trust me. I know. I'm very smart.

117.

Half-Assed Job

"So I make a lot of small mistakes. Ok, now and then I've missed something important, but what nobody seems to appreciate is that my ideas are really amazing. My boss is a mundane nitpicker."

Missing details is typical of ADDers. Perhaps, as they write, in their rush to capture the next brilliant idea, they don't notice what they're actually writing now. They're not catching mistakes as they write. Or spotting them if they even bother to proofread. They skim over what's actually on the page. One solution? They should team up with someone who can proof their work. If they spot small mistakes, great. If they spot big mistakes, even better!

Knowing I wasn't great with numbers, details and contracts, doing big television productions was scary at first. Luckily, I discovered there is an accountant who does the accounting, a production manager who manages the production and a lawyer who does the lying… er… lawying thing.

118.

A *Tangled* World Wide Web

"Surfing the Internet is against company policy, but I figured no one would know. YouTube, Craig's List, eBay … then I got into porn. Within a week my boss and some IT fellow came to my office and confronted me with my downloads. Why do I do these stupid things? I mean, I have the Internet at home."

ADDers push limits. They figure, "Who came up with these stupid rules? Who am I hurting, really?" ADDers minimize risk, creating a pseudo-omnipotence so that they do not fear authority. They can bend any rule, from insider trading to stealing paper from the photocopier. During a late night work marathon, when the offices are empty, they might sneak around rummaging through people's drawers. They love the novelty of what they might find! And the Internet? Well, that's just a billion drawers full of novelties and surprises

I always maintained that the Internet is a dangerous, wasteful cesspool of scams, misinformation and trivial diversions. Until I actually got online. OMG! Heaven! Every link offers the promise of "something new". I have multiple pages open, a dozen streams of stuff I'm interested in, or had no idea I was interested in… and now and then through random chance, I actually stumble across whatever it was I went looking for in the first place. ADHD should be called "Browser Brain."

119.

Cubicle *Cage*

"I work in a 6'x6' pen. There are 30 other caged chickens with me, pecking on their phones in adjacent cubicles; their voices forming a dull drone. The occasional aroma of hot lunches or farts breaks up the grey monotony. Boss rooster drops in pretending to be interested. The air grows thin. The clock hands stop moving. I drift of into daydreams… Kill me now!"

ADDers are bored beyond belief and the cubicle is their hell. The solution is to actively manage their sensory inputs. This means making changes and accommodations to their work space. Adding in pleasant smells, visual pleasantries, bright lights, comfortable furniture, using noise reduction systems, and putting blinds over the windows. It might seem like a lot to ask for but the quality of the work environment is critical to their success.

Your boss probably won't care that customizing your workspace will help with your ADHD. But trust me, your boss will care when you explain that it will increase your productivity, and the company's profits, thus allowing him more time to suck at golf.

120.

Brilliant Non-Producer

"I have some great ideas, but then later on I can't remember them. I figured the secret would be to carry a pen and paper and capture the ideas as they come to me. But of course, a pen and paper is something you have to remember..."

Great inventors like Edison and Da Vinci, display many of the signs of ADHD. For example, Da Vinci started far more paintings than he finished and drew up or jotted down hundreds of ideas but never followed through on them. The ADHD mind can indeed be intuitive, creative and inventive. But don't mistake aimless mental gymnastics for genius.

At some points I've been working on two different TV series and a live theatre production at the same time. Generating ideas? No problem. Capturing them? That's the secret.

If Leonardo Da Vinci had carried around a pocket voice recorder and a notepad he'd be rich by now.

Chapter Eleven

Unconsciously Compensating

By adulthood you have probably found ways to compensate for your ADHD. If it has been undiagnosed until now, you will have developed your coping strategies by trial and error.

Yes, some of the strategies you've unconsciously developed will be quite clever, perhaps unique, oftentimes just what a doctor or an ADHD Coach would have recommended.

The point of getting a proper, reliable diagnosis is to save time and avoid the trial and errors.

This chapter reveals strategies that you may have developed independently. They are common "adjustments" that ADDers make to get through the day. Some work well, others are, at best, a stop gap.

121.

The *Dopamine* Bong

"I'm really creative but I need to smoke a joint before I work. I dunno why, but it helps. I could stop, I'm sure, but it just gets me into the zone so I can focus."

What are the top drugs ADDers abuse or use to self-medicate? Cigarettes, alcohol and cannabis (65)

One of my best friends was a pot head. He'd argue that, "Cannabis is natural; grown by God." And I'd think to myself, "Yeah? So are snake venom, goat feces and arsenic. Natural doesn't mean good for you."

Dr. J ADHD kids often argue, "I want to be in control of what I put in my body, not my parents." As if their drug dealer is a friend who has their best interest at heart! Yes, cannabis is dopamine-based, but it doesn't target the key areas of the ADHD brain, it goes everywhere, and in big enough doses that it strips away motivation.

122.

Pulling *All–Nighter*s

"I leave things to the last minute and cram. I go into this zone of sleep deprivation for a day or so, until the work is mostly done and then I crash. I pull all-nighters and sleep all weekend. It's just how I work."

Sleep is not like money: a human can't run up a deficit during the week and then pay it back on the weekend. Regular sleep enhances brain activity and concentration (66). However, cramming is a study style that makes sleep an inconvenience. ADDers excel in a crisis, so many learn to create a crisis-like state when they need motivation. For example a last-minute, all-night cram session gives the ADDer a rush of adrenaline. Fear and pressure wakes them up, and they get it done.

Yes, I'd get it done, but always with a sickly feeling of, "Why did I leave it so late?" Before the diagnosis I lived in a self-generated state of stress. Once I understood waiting till the last minute was my way of producing enough adrenaline to get moving, I found a better way to overcome procrastination. I just start. One step. However small. "I'll do a few minutes and then stop." But the momentum from that first accomplishment, no matter how simple, propels me forward. To the next step. And the next. Suddenly the train is rolling, and I hop on.

123.

Home Body

"I'd rather be alone in my workshop doing a project than at a big social event. The sad thing is, my wife loves being around people and wishes we went out more. I'm not Rain Man, but I find social situations stressful."

The hustle and bustle of crowded places overwhelms the ADDer's already limited ability to filter out a lot of incoming information. Their sensory systems are unable to deal with the 'shock and awe'. Whereas at home, in familiar surroundings, the ADDer is not bombarded with extraneous stimulation, and naturally feels more comfortable.

Once I understood ADHD is about 'filtering' I could see why a noisy, crowded sports bar, with a hundred voices, a dozen TV's, and mobs of waiters singing Happy Birthday every 3 minutes made me so hyper. At first it can be exhilarating. I'm on. It's fun. But as the noise level rises, there's a tipping point: Fun, fun, fun… Then frustration, consternation and agitation! Check, please!

124.

First Course: *Dessert*

"As a kid I hated waiting to my open birthday presents. At College I'd play video games before I studied. And if I have a big assignment to do, I'm all over it. Unless someone wants to go to a movie. Or there's something on TV. Or I want a snack. Or I'd rather go biking…"

Most adults understand that you work and then reap the rewards. Many ADDers have this sequence wrong; they want their fun now and promise to get around to work later. This may well be a result of impatience and failing to consider the long-term consequences related to their responsibilities. Unfortunately, they miss the pride and relief that comes from having something finished.

I often confuse pleasure with happiness, or comfort with deep satisfaction. I want to have my cake and eat it too. And to eat your piece as well. But if I have the fun first I don't really enjoy it, because the unfinished work is a nagging incompletion hanging over me. Doing things backwards is stressful. In fact desserts backwards spells stressed!

I've learned to strike a deal with myself—one mouthful of dessert after three mouthfuls of veggies. (Okay, this isn't how I eat, but you get the idea.) When I can parcel out my rewards, I have endless motivators, and I can stick to something far longer.

125.

G.I. *Joe*

"I was in the military and I loved it. The Marines used to have that recruiting slogan, 'We get more done by 8 a.m. than most people do in a day.' And it was true. I was productive. I contributed. Pulling my weight. I felt unstoppable."

Ironically, an organization with strict rules, such as the police or military, can work for an ADDer. Why? It seems ADDers are less stressed when decision making is clear, authority figures are well defined, work expectations are established, there is a common purpose, a sense of unity, and work is tactile or physical. Structure makes them calm, freeing them to be very productive.

This may also explain why ADDers often work for, or marry, people who nag and control them. They remember the one year when they did well in school was with a very strict teacher. (They may forget that the teacher also cared about the ADDer and had earned their respect.)

A stage show has a specific, immutable deadline. It's called, "Opening Night." The tickets are sold, people are coming. As the evening approaches, the director takes charge, stopping any bickering and cracking the whip. There is no longer a time or place for gossiping, nastiness or personal histrionics. (We save that stuff for "Closing Night" when everyone has had a few drinks.)

126.

Fitness *Freak*

"I started exercising and loved it. I was at the gym all the time, working out. It felt incredible. And it's good for me, right? But now my trainer warns me that I'm overdoing it."

Exercise wakes up the body and produces lots of 'happy' chemicals. But those chemicals can be addictive. Being hooked on exercise sounds better than being addicted to gambling, drugs, or sex, but if a person is going to the gym because they crave the 'fix' of good chemicals then it becomes another form of self-medicating.

While training for a 622 km bike rally I got into the best shape of my life. (Which I admit, isn't saying much.) Two months into training, my body actually began to crave exercise. The way I normally crave food. It was bizarre realizing, "I want to go ride for an hour." During the actual bike rally the chatter in my brain died away. I had moments of Zen. Which was amazing, considering how badly my bum hurt.

127.

Opposites *Attract*

"When we started dating, she was everything that I wasn't: detail oriented, conscientious, orderly, thoughtful and nurturing. However, after ten years and two children her constant correcting and questioning everything I do ticks me off. I am not a child!"

Love is chemical. Opposites attract. It is a biological mating process, so an impulsive person is drawn to a partner who likes detail and planning. (67) This union has huge advantages because their complimentary strengths provide a robust balance. But only if they can respect their differences and work together. Unfortunately, opposites have a tendency to self-destruct if the couple cannot establish the path to the middle ground.

My wife's biggest challenge is learning to separate me from my ADHD. Whereas my biggest challenge is appreciating that she's not nagging-- she loves me and wants to help. One day when things weren't going well, and my defenses were bristling, she looked me in the eyes and said, "Baby, I'm on your side." I got it. When I get prickly, I remind myself she's my biggest supporter. The right partner can make all the difference.

128.

My *Post-it* Passion

"I stick Post-it Notes® everywhere. I even fill my agenda with Post-its® so that tasks that didn't get done today are easily moved to tomorrow's page. And I love throwing the paper into the recycling bin when I have completed a task. It's good for the planet and me."

Post-it Notes® can be an ADDer's savior. They are fast, colorful, easy to use and the right size to deal with the broad issue of memory impairment. Plus they can be transferred from one place to another. Amazing!

Our documentary ADD and Loving It!? was built around Post-it Notes®. Both on camera and during production. But like with real estate, it's location, location, location. The note needs to be right on my keyboard so that I cannot start working without reading it. Post that same note a few inches to the side of my keyboard? I may not notice it until three weeks later.

But I can also overdo it, putting reminders everywhere until they blend into a pastel explosion and then disappear into the background, like wallpaper.

129.

Electronic *Ecstasy*

"My girlfriend says I am a techno-junkie, but it helps me organize myself to have an iPad, an iPhone and an iPod to supplement my MacBook Air and Powerbook... What?"

Electronics might be the salvation for the ADDer. The faster the world moves, the more these electronic devices can help ADDers cope. Hardware and software advances have been critical to help circumvent some of the processing issues that ADDers have. The dilemma is that these devices are so novel and addictive, they can become an obsession in themselves. As well, they're expensive, and every six months there's another slew of even more powerful versions that the ADDer just has to have.

I remember manual typewriters, carbon paper and white-out smeared all over the page, my hands and my clothes. What ecstasy when I bought my first Mac back in 1984. The visual of the desktop made such sense. Everything laid out logically, all in view, easy to sort... Since then the gadgets have gotten even more seductive. "Look, yet another function I'll never use!" No wonder Silicon Valley is nicknamed 'ADHD Central.'

130.

Secretarial *Success*

"My secretary did everything I hated to do. She would manage my schedule and keep everything organized. She was an older lady who had this librarian-like no-nonsense attitude. Best of all, she would lie for me when I was behind or stuck on something. You can't pay enough for that!"

Delegating is a very positive coping strategy and it is cost effective. Sometimes the ADDer thinks, "I will end up having to do it myself anyway, because they can't do it as well as I can." Delegating, when combined with effective training and clear instructions, frees up considerable time and is key to success. But finding the right people to delegate to is key. Hire someone with an even temperament, who is detail oriented and can carry a task to completion. In some ways the opposite of the ADDer.

In the early days, I performed in a small troupe at local comedy clubs. It was a lean, mean production and we could handle everything, onstage and off. Later, doing a television series, I had to delegate because there was so much to be done. The trick is to find people who deliver on what they promise, when you clearly explain what needs doing. At first they take longer than I would, and I'm tempted to wade in and do it myself, but they soon have it mastered, freeing me up to do my thing… comedy. And, of course, bossing people around with a bullwhip.

131.

"*No*" Man

"I never said, "No" to my boss, fearing it would damage my career. I wanted to please her and prove she could rely on me. But I've learned the hard way that it's better to deliver on what I promise than to over commit."

People want deliverables, not broken promises. It is OK to say "No". If the boss continues to put pressure on, then say, "OK, I have all of these projects. This is how long they will take. Which ones do you want me to work on first, knowing that the others will have to wait?" The ADDer is not suggesting they can't do the work, simply asserting themselves by seeking clarity in defining their priorities.

Another ADHD mantra: Promise + Deliver = Respect.

When someone outlines an idea they have for a TV show my minds starts humming, ideas start popping and suddenly I've volunteered to help, having forgotten everything I'm supposed to be doing. Which is bad if I'm driving the car at the time. It's as if the exciting new project causes temporary amnesia and I need a moment to recall, "Oh yeah, I'm already doing three TV shows." I've learned to say, "Let me get back to you." When I do call back and explain why I have to say no, they always understand. Who knew?

132.

Desiderata

"The Desiderata is an amazing poem. I repeat the words of this little prayer-like compilation of truths whenever I need perspective. It is refreshing. Calming. It stops the rush of doubt. I especially like where it says, "Be interested in your own career, however humble, it is a real possession in the changing fortunes of time." That helps me to stop comparing myself to others and just focus on my goals."

 When I first read the poem Desiderata, I was amazed. It is like a form of Cognitive Behavioral Therapy: it speaks about life's truths and about positive, forward thinking. It explains how to distinguish false, negative beliefs and thus avoid errors of perception. This is really fundamental. Desiderata is the epitome of the internal voice that we all need to carry.

 I like anything that is in the public domain and free. Check out TotallyADD.com. (That was subtle. I should be in sales.)

Chapter Twelve

Amazing, Unexpected, Sometimes Hidden, Often Unappreciated Strengths of ADHD Adults

Finally, some GOOD NEWS! (Bet you turned to this chapter first!)

The fact is that ADDers can flourish. ADHD responds well to treatment and a holistic approach can measurably reduce impairment.

But in this chapter we suggest how some of your ADHD impairments can become strengths, and you don't have to change at all. You simply change the context.

Even some core areas of impairment can work to your advantage in certain circumstances.

Yes, you are built differently, but different can be good. Your unique combination of traits may allow you to see things that no one else appreciates or understands.

And this is important. For you and for the world. Outdated beliefs and practices are behind many of humanity's problems. People who can see things from a fresh perspective are the hope of the world.

133.

Creative *Calm*

"My best mark in High School was always Art. I had a flair for visual stuff, even fashion and design. When I was creating I felt great. But mom always warned me, 'Artists all starve.' Now that I make a living in graphic arts, my Mom brags to her friends how I have always been 'so creative'"

Impulsivity and Creativity. They are different, but definitely related. Creativity may show up as strong problem-solving abilities, a visual/artistic sense, kinesthetic skills, or even a gift for music. When ADDers have a talent, their ability to think outside the box can inspire unique connections and startling, fresh ideas.

When something is due, like this chapter, and it's late, the positive pressure wakes me up. Zing, Pop, Pow! Ideas start flowing. I can barely type fast enough. It's intense; all consuming. It's not random rambling; I'm focused, intentional, in the zone. Hours zoom by until, suddenly, the chapter is finished… and my bladder is about to burst… Excuse me! Out of the way! Coming through!…

134.

Natural Born Entrepreneur

"Even at 16, I couldn't see myself working for someone else. With my inventive mind, I figured I'd be good at business. My parents were angry that I quit College, until I made my first million. Since then I've started three more companies. Two failed, but I learned a ton."

Many ADDers can focus their drive for a highly charged reward, namely money. Money means power. Control. Freedom. It's a strong motivator.

When they feel in charge of their destiny, ADDers make the rules and accept the consequences. Avoiding responsibility vanishes. 'Being responsible' is no longer about blame, but about receiving credit.

In my practice, I treat lots of people who are struggling, but also many Fortune 500 execs, Olympic and professional athletes, and celebrities. They come to see me because their child has ADHD. They are in shock, feeling powerless about their child's issues. Yet this disorder, ADHD, sounds familiar to them. They recognize the symptoms in themselves and realize they have succeeded by overcompensating with hyper-focusing and hard work.

I have non-ADHD friends who are terrified when their employer starts downsizing, "What will I do?!" Changing jobs strikes them as terrifying. My friends want predictability; that would drive me crazy. As an ADDer, working in TV is perfect. I get to write, act, direct, and produce. We finish one show and then it's, "What next?" The future feels wide open.

135.

*Brain*stormer

"Lots of people come to me with problems because I'm good at solving them. Even with gadgets, I'm able to figure out how they work. I can walk into a business or situation that I know nothing about, and pretty soon I'm offering all kinds of ideas. Some are too off-the-wall, but often they say, 'That's brilliant! Why didn't we think of that?'"

The ADDer truly can see the forest, but not the trees. In fact, they may walk head first into the trees. This 'big picture' ability. to stand above it all, can allow them to see how an intricate machine works, or to figure out a complex system, such as the stock market. Is this because they have an ability to synthesize a lot of information quickly? Or do they enjoy the novelty of a puzzle? Either way, ADDers are good at paradigm shifting and cross-disciplinary thinking.

My friend Malcolm has ADHD up the wazoo. And he works with it, big time. Talk about out-of-the-box thinking, he actually invented his own unique career. He drives around industrial areas, stopping at factories that look interesting. He saunters in and asks what they do and how they do it. Then he leaves, does some brainstorming, and returns with all kinds of ideas on how to increase productivity, save energy, reduce costs, or even start whole new product lines. He loves it. So do his clients. And so does his bank balance.

136.

Once upon *a time...*

"My aunt always warned my mom that I needed to play with real kids rather than talking to imaginary people. Or she claimed I lied a lot. I'm imaginative and perhaps I 'embellish' a bit but I love that look of wonder people have when they're caught up in what I'm saying. Nowadays, I entertain my children with my made-up stories. Perhaps I should become a children's author, or heck, a politician."

 The combination of verbal skills, creativity, a sense of fun, and a youthful spirit makes one a great storyteller. Perhaps telling stories started out as an adaptive strategy, to avoid blame for yet another screw up. But the fun and novelty have kept it going. These ADDers become master story tellers.

 Story telling isn't just for screenwriters. Or novelists. The best non-fiction books tell a story. In the newsroom editors ask, "What's the story?" Advertisers try to tell a story—and not just with words; every great photograph tells a story. So does every painting... What I'm trying to say here would probably have more impact if I turned it into a story.

137.

Class *Clown*

"I'm funny. Being charming and disarming has saved me from a lot of my screw ups. Sometimes I can't tell if they're laughing at me or with me, you know? And sometimes it crosses a line and people get huffy. But I like this part of me."

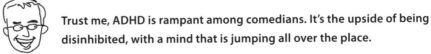

Many ADDers become the class clown as a way of coping. Later, if they can develop a sense of humor about themselves, they become strong and resilient. Humor becomes a tremendous tool and a mature defense.

In adults, humor is connected to heightened sexuality (i.e. humor is attractive), increased morale (i.e. people want to be around you), stronger goal orientation (i.e. people who can laugh persevere through hardships, even danger) and more optimism (i.e. humor is a cognitive construct to overcome depression).

Trust me, ADHD is rampant among comedians. It's the upside of being disinhibited, with a mind that is jumping all over the place.

I vividly recall my first time on stage; the annual school-show. There I am, the shy, Grade 10 nerd, getting huge laughs! Suddenly girls notice me, smile at me, even talk to me! (Instantly I know what I'm going to be doing for a living!)

138.

Breadth *versus* Depth

"When I get interested in something, I have to know everything. I buy all the books and equipment, then, just as suddenly, I'm on to something new. Last year I started Yoga, then switched to Pilates, until I heard about Tai Chi! I'm a jack of all trades."

Commitment can be a challenge for an ADDer when there is always a dozen 'What ifs' clamoring for attention. But the upside is that the person follows their curiosity to develop a wide range of interests, skills and knowledge.

Once ADDers do take the plunge and find something they like, they can develop a powerful sense of purpose and become champions. Their ability to hyper-focus becomes endurance, and is one of their biggest strengths.

I used to believe I lacked willpower. Now I've decided I'm just naturally inquisitive and open to new things. The things I tried and liked, I kept doing; including magic, which requires a ton of focus and attention. Go ahead, ma'am, think of a card... Queen of Hearts, right?

As for the Indian cooking, Hawaiian guitar, juggling, Swing Dancing, pasta making, flute, and bocce that I tried and abandoned? Well, they just didn't give me any juice. Now you, sir, think of a card? Ace of Spades, right? Thanks! For my next trick...

139.

Adventure Time

"Friends love my enthusiasm and envy my willingness to try new things. New places, new people, new worlds; I'm game for anything. Hey, you only live once; if it doesn't work out, so what? I had fun trying."

Impulsivity can get someone into trouble, but spontaneity can make life very interesting. When someone is on their death bed their biggest regrets are what they didn't do. I suspect ADHD people die smiling. They tackle their Bucket List early. Furthermore, their willingness to pursue new ideas, when it's balanced with common sense, can also be a huge advantage in business. Or in dating. Or in the depth of their worldliness. ADDers who follow their spontaneity will develop a joyful, eternal optimism. They become explorers in every realm of life. Every day can be an adventure.

When I was 51 years old I impulsively agreed to do a 622 km charity bike rally. Even though I hadn't been on a bike in decades, didn't own a bike and was completely out of shape. It turned out to be the most fun I've ever had with my pants on. Well, not pants, they were weird bicycle shorts. One time, on a sharp turn... never mind.

140.

Rescue Ranger

"I save people every day. Literally. I am an ER doctor. The bigger the crisis, the better the day. The problem starts when my shift is over; it takes me a while to turn off the adrenaline and get my paperwork done. The rest of my life could seem boring by comparison, but my husband reminds me to take time to unwind. And he does lots of things to keep our life interesting."

What overwhelms the average person's faculties seems to bring the ADHD brain to full alertness. Firefighters, police officers, military personnel, journalists, and social workers all do well when ADHD is part of their profile. They respond to crises. They feel for the victims. They understand the depth of despair.

A firefighter, who drives the big ladder trucks, told me, "When I race down the streets, the cars part before me, like I'm Moses. If there is a child in distress I drive even faster, passing cars on either side with just inches to spare. I am so 'on', I feel unstoppable."

Years ago the nighttime silence was shattered by an ominous drone, roaring across our neighbourhood like an Alien from War of The Worlds. Deafening! Everyone cowered inside and called 911. Not me. Armed with a hockey stick, I roamed the streets searching for the 'Alien.' No one joined me. Turned out to be an obsolete air raid siren that accidentally turned itself on. How disappointing.

141.

All Sensors *Wide Open*

"I love when I have a phone in my ear, a pencil in my hand and I'm driving with my knees. It's like my brain has many brains all working simultaneously."

The ADHD mind can be like a thermostat: it only switches on once the temperature reaches a certain level. When the load increases and the demand on their attention gets high enough, the ADDer seems to click on and they're up and running. A small task doesn't engage their mind; the brain can't be bothered. But multiple small tasks can add up, the load becomes big enough and suddenly they're motivated, hyper-alert and super productive.

One way I wake up my brain is to create games, or challenges. For example, when I'm watching hockey, I pop up during the commercials and see how many things I can tidy, sort or put away. I get to see The Toronto Maple Leafs lose another game and I finish three loads of laundry, tidy four rooms, while earning my wife's undying gratitude. (Nudge nudge.)

142.

King of Commissions

"I am the modern version of the hunter-gatherer: the consummate salesperson. I can sell anything because I can talk the talk and read people. Closing the deal is a total rush. I maximize my commissions, putting me in the top one percent in my field. But for a long time, my invoicing and follow up were a mess. Till I hired my assistant."

A huge percentage of my clients work in sales: real estate agents, product sales people, pharmaceutical reps, stock brokers, and, yes, Amway Associates. They love commission sales. Networking and making social connections are a thrill. They succeed because their job is so goal-oriented. The most successful salespeople make sure they have someone to follow up on their paperwork—the billing and invoicing—leaving them free to do what they do best. Sell, sell, sell.

I actually sold a history channel on the idea of doing a skit-comedy show. And I sold them on the idea of renewing us for five seasons. Recently I sold a big network on the idea of letting me make a documentary about a comedian with Adult ADHD. Even more amazing, I sold my wife on the idea of marrying me. I haven't invoiced her yet. I'm behind on the paperwork.

143.

The *Apple* of My iPhone™

"At age 8, I made my own computer. By age 10, I was programming. I became a computer game developer when I was 20, and a multi-millionaire by 25. That year I retired to an atoll in the South Pacific! After six months I was going stir crazy. I came back to start a new company. It's going great."

Internet and dot-com businesses are full of ADHD people: computer programmers, graphic designers, web developers, software engineers, hardware specialists, IT personnel, and game designers. Behind the safety of the keyboard, they can become anyone they want to be. This new virtual realm offers them freedom, because there are no 'old hands' telling them 'it can't be done'. Anything is possible, and ADDers rise to the challenge.

I love technology for where it can take me, what it allows me to do. It's a tool. The ultimate tool. I mean where else can I become a Pint-Size, Purple, Lesbian Spell Caster? Certainly not at home anymore, after that incident where… Never mind.

144.

A *Star* Performer

"When I was young my aunt took me to a Broadway musical. Incredible. They got to dress up and use their imagination. It was magical and I was in heaven. I knew that's what I would do for a living. Stage fright? Never even considered it."

Whenever our documentary ADD & Loving It?! airs we do publicity interviews. And almost every D.J. or Talk Radio host admits they have ADHD. And the music industry is full of ADHD too. Hey, that's why songs are three minutes long.

Comedy as well. You only have to look at the number of comedians who are 'out and open' about their ADHD to realize Improv comedy attracts this mindset. I'll say stuff onstage about bowel regularity that I wouldn't even ask my doctor. Especially after she laughed and yelled Encore!

Remember that childhood Hyperactive/Impulsivity can transform by adulthood into a 'pressure to talk.' Many adults who have not yet got a diagnosis are instinctively drawn to 'talky' jobs: teacher, auctioneer, salesperson. Minister, Rabbi, or Iman, tour guide, sports announcer, hairdresser, Hollywood gossip columnist. Yes, even politician.

145.

Needle in a *Haystack*

"I'll walk into a store and almost instantly sense if they carry what I want, or not. It drives my wife crazy."

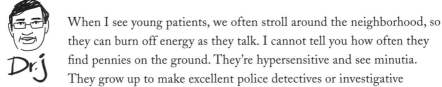

At the antique market I'm scanning the booths like The Terminator. "Nothing." "Nope." "This won't have anything." It's automatic. Until, "Bingo!" I sense this booth will be good. I dart in and look around, sometimes for several minutes, before spotting the thing I instinctively noticed in my quick scan. Bizarre. When my wife catches up I show her what I spotted, "Look! It's exactly what I wanted." She is impressed, then reminds me, "You already bought one last time we were here." "Oh, right." Great acuity. Crappy memory.

When I see young patients, we often stroll around the neighborhood, so they can burn off energy as they talk. I cannot tell you how often they find pennies on the ground. They're hypersensitive and see minutia. They grow up to make excellent police detectives or investigative journalists. Earning way more than pennies.

146. The *Go-To* Gal!

"People love my energy, eagerness and enthusiasm."

If I'm interested and enthused about something I can leave the Energizer Bunny choking on my exhaust fumes.

And others want to feel that energy. But not be overwhelmed by it. The ADDer must find balance, because once harnessed, the strength of enthusiasm is a goldmine.

 P.S.: By 'exhaust fumes', I didn't mean farting.

 You sure about that, Rick?!

147. Heal Others, *Heal Thyself*

"I am drawn to people who are suffering, to the poor, to animals in distress, to appeals from charities."

Having felt like a victim, ADDers are gratified by helping the outcasts and downtrodden. They make great social workers, child/youth workers or crusading attorneys.

In the Forums on www.TotallyADD.com it seems like there's an unspoken rule, "We're all in this together. No one left behind." Love it.

148. Mentorific

"When I contribute to someone else's success, part of me is in them."

Giving back. Paying it forward. Knowing the pain of their own journey a successful ADDer becomes an inspirational teacher because they themselves struggled in 'the system.'

When Patrick and Janis McKenna shared their story in ADD & Loving It?!, thousands were helped. We all felt we owed it to our children, and every child... Okay, now I'm just getting soppy.

149. Little League *Lawyer*

"As a kid, I would argue over every loophole in my parent's rules. Once I saved a kid from detention by arguing his case. My teacher forgave me."

When I see kids like this, I smile and assure the parents, "Just hang in there, he'll be a very smart attorney someday."

Trial attorneys are performers, creating drama. No wonder actors love playing them. If I'm wrong, get a lawyer and sue me.

150. *Hands* On

"I was smart, but grades sucked. But I loved customizing cars and doing woodworking. Now, I build custom kitchens for a living and restore cars as a hobby."

Physical activity that is spatial, tactile, precise and creative seems to engage the ADHD mind. Be it bricklaying or sculpting, ADDers are often great with their hands.

I love doing renovations. And performing card tricks. Building models. Playing darts. Grabbing my wife. All at the same time. (Okay, there's that multi-tasking again.)

151. *Athletic* Juice

"I was an Olympian. After retiring, I felt lost. Luckily I discovered coaching young athletes."

For my patients who are professional athletes the structure, intense training, mentorship and clear goals alleviates their ADHD. When their careers end they must find a 'new game' to play.

While training for a 622 km bike rally, my ADHD decreased dramatically. Now I need a new challenge. Naked pole vaulting? "Oh, he clipped the bar! That's going to leave a mark!"

152. Soap *Boxer*

"I am a politician. I love the crowds. I love fighting for the underdog. I love the camera. I love taking on big causes and the accolades that come from pulling it off."

Think of successful politicians—talkative, energizing, charismatic, smart, drawn to causes—and you think of the ADDer.

And their ADHD means they probably have a higher rate of scandalous mistakes in their past, which investigative journalists will dig up. Since many journalists have ADHD, it's win-win!

153. Kid *Tested*

"I love working with kids. Maybe because I still am one inside. Early on I was a babysitter, then a camp counselor. Now? I'm a pediatrician."

Not everyone can work with kids. It demands patience and empathy. If you still feel like a child sometimes, then working with kids can be very rewarding. Trust me.

When we visit friends who have small kids it doesn't take long before they're yelling, "Do that magic trick again! Make another crayon appear out of Ryan's nose!"

154. Justice for *All*

"As an advocate I refuse to be intimidated. I will fight for my family, my community and my world, and win."

Mothers of ADD kids know the battleground. I often find they can deal with their own ADHD issues by becoming advocates for their children. Even for all children.

It's amazing how many people on the TotallyADD.com website are eager to help each other find answers, move forward and overcome obstacles. Love it.

155. Future *Focus*

"I love my kids more than anything else in the world. I'd do anything for them. I'd take on the whole world for them. I'd even get my own ADHD handled."

There is HOPE for the next generation. It's YOU.

Index

Numbers in this index refer to each of the 155 different signs of ADHD found in this book, not to page numbers. For example, *Absent Mindedness* is found in Sign 59, *Yeast? It said yeast?*.

Imaging 34

Immaturity 16, 66

Impairing symptoms 1, 4, 5, 18

Impatience 65, 69, 72

Impulsiveness 4, 14, 18, 22, 25, 45, 54, 58, 67, 71, 74, 107

Inattention 14, 31, 50, 55, 59

Inattentive Subtype 4

Injustice 147

Insensitive 116

Intensity (see also hyperfocus) 146

Instinctive 29, 35, 141,

Instructions 35

Intelligence 17, 21

Internal dialogue 132

Interest 138

Interest charges 111

Internalizing 4, 26, 80

Internet 29, 33, 118, 143, 148

Interrupting 1, 43, 61, 65

Intrusive 104

Intuition 35, 135, 145

Inventive (see also creative) 92, 120, 135

J

Jerks 104

Job
   changes 39
   fired 39

Journalists 140, 145, 152

Judgment, poor 18

Justifying 101

Justice 154

K

Kryptonite 109

L

Last minute 49, 103

Late fees 111

Lateness 51

Lawyer 45, 46, 147, 149, 152

LD 76

Leadership 148, 154

Learned helplessness 73

Learning 15
   disorders 21, 76
   strategies 55

Legal 81

License suspensions 43

Lifespan 7

Lifestyle 126

Light therapy 90

Linear thinking 51

Line-ups 69

Listening 61, 97, 98

Lists 31, 52, 93

Losing 99

Love 127

Lump and Dump 109

M

Manic-depression (see bipolar) 78

Mantra 109, 115, 131

Marijuana (see also cannabis) 24, 84 121

Marital problems (see also divorce) 71

Marriage 13, 127

Materialism 109

Media 106

Medical examination 82, 83

Medicating, self 24, 25, 36, 84, 144

Medications 73

Melodrama 136

Memory 50, 56, 58, 128

Mental energy 50, 141

Mentorship 112, 148

Military 125, 140

Mindfulness 50, 58, 70

Minimal Brain Dysfunction 3

Misdiagnosis 63, 73, 78, 79, 80, 82, 84

Mistakes 45, 59, 116, 117

Money 42, 110, 113

Monitoring 87, 88

References

1. American Psychiatric Association (APA). (2000). *Diagnostic and statistical manual of mental disorders* (4th ed., text rev.). Washington, DC: Author

2. Hoffmann H. (1948). *Der Struwwelpeter. Oder lustige Geschichten und drollige Bilder für Kinder von 3 bis 6 Jahren.* Loewes, Stuttgart: Frankfurter Originalausgabe

3. Still, G.F. (1902), Some abnormal psychical conditions in children: the Goulstonian lectures. *Lancet, 1,* 1008-1012, 1077-1082, 1163-1168.

4. Strauss, A.A., & Lehtinen, L.E. (1947). *Psychopathology and education of the brain-injured child.* New York: Grune & Stratton.

5. Laufer, M.W., Denhoff, E., & Solomons, G. (1957). Hyperkinetic impulse disorder in children's behavior problems. *Psychosomatic Medicine,* 19(1), 38-49.

6. Weiss, G., & Hechtman, L.T. (1993). *Hyperactive children grown up: ADHD in children, adolescents and adults* (2nd ed.). New York: Gilford Press.

7. Kessler, R.C., Adler, L., Barkley, R.A., Biederman, J., Conners, C.K., Demler, O., et al. (2006). The prevalence and correlates of adult ADHD in the United States: Results from the National Co-morbidity Survey Replication. *American Journal of Psychiatry, 163,* 716-723.

8. American Psychiatric Association (APA). (2000). *Diagnostic and statistical manual of mental disorders* (4th ed., text rev.). Washington, DC: Author

9. Barkley, R. A., Murphy, K.R., Fischer, M. (2010) ADHD in Adults. Gilford Press, NY, 32-35

10. Faraone, S.V., & Doyle, A.E. (2001). The nature and heritability of attention-deficit/hyperactivity disorder. *Child and Adolescent Psychiatric Clinics of North America, 10*(2), 299-316.

11. Laufer, M.W., Denhoff, E., & Solomons, G. (1957). Hyperkinetic impulse disorder in children's behavior problems. *Psychosomatic Medicine, 19*(1), 38-49.

12. Weiss, G., & Hechtman, L.T. (1993). *Hyperactive children grown up: ADHD in children, adolescents and adults* (2nd ed.). New York: Gilford Press.

13. Mannuzza, S., & Klein, R. (1992). Adult psychiatric status of hyperactive boys grown up. *American Journal of Psychiatry, 155,* 493-498.

14. Barkley, R.A., Fischer, M., Edelbrock, C.S., & Smallish, L. (1990). The adolescent outcome of hyperactive children diagnosed by research criteria: 1. An 8-year prospective follow-up study. *Journal of the American Academy of Child and Adolescent Psychiatry, 29*(4), 546-557.

15. Okie S. (2006). ADHD in adults. *New England Journal of Medicine.* 354:2637–2641.

16. Cunningham, C.E. & Boyle, M.H. (2002). Preschoolers at risk for attention-deficit hyperactivity disorder and oppositional defiant disorder: Family, parenting and behavioral correlates. *Journal of Abnormal Child Psychology, 30*(6), 555-569.

17. Barkley, R.A., ADHD Update, *Presented at the 4th Annual Meeting of the Canadian ADHD Resource Alliance*, October 17, 2008, Montreal, Canada.

18. Ginsberg, Y., Hirvikoski, T., & Lindefors, N. (2010). Attention deficit hyperactivity disorder among prison inmates is a prevalent, persistent and disabling disorder. *BMC Psychiatry, 10*(112), 1187-1471.

19. Bussing, R., Zima, B. T., & Perwien, A. R. (2000). Self-esteem in special education children with ADHD: Relationship to disorder charcteristics and medication use. *Journal of the American Academy of Child and Adolescent Psychiatry, 39*(10), 1260-1269.

20. Brehaut, J. C., Miller, A., Raina, P., & McGrail, K. M. (2003). Childhood behavior disorders and injuries among children and youth: a population-based study. *Pediatrics, 111*(2), 262-269.

21. Pomerleau, O.F., Downey, K.K., Stelson, F.W., Pomerleau, C.S. (1995).Cigarette Smoking in adult patients diagnosed with Attention Deficit Hyperactivity Disorder. *Journal of Substance Abuse, 7*, 373-378.

22. Halperin, J.M., Newcorn, J. H., Koda, V. H., Pick, L., McKay, K.E., & Knott, P. (1997). Noradrenergic mechanisms in ADHD children with and without reading disabilities: A replication and extension. *Journal of the American Academy of Child and Adolescent Psychiatry, 36*(12), 1688-1697.

23. Barkley, R.A. (1997). Attention-deficit/hyperactivity disorder, self-regulation, and time: Toward a more comprehensive theory. *Journal of Developmental Pediatrics, 18*(4), 271-279.

24. Zametkin, A.J., Nordahl, T.E., Gross, M., King, A.C., Semple, W.E., Rumsey, J., et al.(1990). Cerebral glucose metabolism in adults with hyperactivity of childhood onset. *New England Journal of Medicine, 323*(20), 1361-1366.

25. Schweitzer, J.B., Lee, D.O., Hanford, R.B. et al. (2003). A positron emission tomography study of methylphenidate in adults with ADHD: Alterations in resting blood flow and predicting treatment response. *Neuropsychopharmacology, 28*, 967-973.

26. Volkow, N. D., & Swanson, J. M. (2003). Variables that affect the clinical use and abuse of methylphenidate in the treatment of ADHD. *American Journal of Psychiatry, 160*(4), 1909-1918.

27. Turner, N.E., Jain, U., Spence, W., & Sangeneh, M. (2008). Pathways to pathological gambling: component analysis of variables related to pathological gambling. *International Gambling Studies, 8*(3), 281-298

28. DiScala, C., Lescohier, I., Barthel, M., & Li, G. (1997). Injuries to children with Attention Deficit Hyperactivity Disorder. *Pediatrics, 102*(6), 1415-1421.

29. Barkley, R.A., Murphy, K. R., DuPaul, G. J., & Bush, T. (2002). Driving in young adults with attention deficit hyperactivity disorder: knowledge, performance, adverse outcomes, and the role of executive functioning. *Journal of the International Neuropsychological Society, 8i*(5), 655-672.

30. Biederman, J., Faraone, S.V., Spencer, T.J., Mick, E., Monuteaux, M.C., & Aleardi, M. (2006). Functional impairments in adults with self-reports of diagnosed ADHD: A controlled study of 1001 adults in the community. *Journal of clinical Psychiatry, 67*(4), 524-540.

31. Pelham, W.E., Molina, B.S., Gnagy, E.M., Wilson, T.K., & Greenhouse, J. B. (2008). Rate and predictors of divorce among parents of youths with ADHD. *Journal of Consulting Psychology, 76*(5), 735-744.

32. Flory, K., Molina, B.S., Pelham, W.E., Smith, B. (2006). Childhood ADHD predicts risky sexual behavior in young adulthood. *Journal of Clinical Child and Adolescent Psychology, 35*(4), 571-577.

33. Barkley, R. A., Fischer, M., Smallish, L., & Fletcher, K. (2006). Young adult outcome of hyperactive children: Adaptive functioning in major life activities. *Journal of the American Academy of Child and Adolescent Psychiatry, 45*(2), 192-202.

34. Barkley, R. A., Fischer, M., Smallish, L., & Fletcher, K. (2006). Young adult outcome of hyperactive children: Adaptive functioning in major life activities. *Journal of the American Academy of Child and Adolescent Psychiatry, 45*(2), 192-202.

35. Biederman, J., Faraone, S.V., Spencer, T.J., Mick, E., Monuteaux, M.C., & Aleardi, M. (2006). Functional impairments in adults with self-reports of diagnosed ADHD: A controlled study of 1001 adults in the community. *Journal of clinical Psychiatry, 67*(4), 524-540.

36. Biederman, J., Faraone, S.V., Spencer, T.J., Mick, E., Monuteaux, M.C., & Aleardi, M. (2006). Functional impairments in adults with self-reports of diagnosed ADHD: A controlled study of 1001 adults in the community. *Journal of clinical Psychiatry, 67*(4), 524-540.

37. Barkley, R.A. (2004). Driving impairments in teens and adults with attention-deficit/hyperactivity disorder. *Psychiatric Clinics of North America, 27*, 233-260.

38. Jerome, L., Segal, A., & Habinski, L. (2006). What we know about ADHD and driving risk: A literature review, meta-analysis and critique. *Journal of the Canadian Academy of Child and Adolescent Psychiatry, 15*(3), 105-125.

39. Babinski, L. M., Hartsough, C. S., & Lambert, N. M. (1999). Childhood conduct problems, hyper-activity-impulsivity and inattention as predictors of criminal behavior. *Journal of Child Psychology and Psychiatry, 40*(3), 347-355.

40. Carlson, C. L., Tamm, L., & Gaub, M. (1997). Gender differences in children with ADHD, ODD and co-occurring ADHD/ODD identified in a school population. *Journal of the American Academy of Child and Adolescent Psychiatry, 36*(12), 1706-1714.

41. Volkow, N., & Swanson, J. M. (2008). Does childhood treatment of ADHD with stimulant medication affect substance abuse in adulthood? *American Journal of Psychiatry, 165*(5), 553-555.

42. Milberger, S., Biederman, J., Faraone, S.V., Chen, L., & Jones, J. (1996). Is maternal smoking during pregnancy a risk factor for attention deficit hyperactivity disorder in children? *American Journal of Psyhciatry, 153*(6), 1138-1142.

43. Barkley, R.A., Fischer, M., Edelbrock, C., & Smallish, L. (1991). The adolescent outcome of hyperactive children diagnosed by research criteria: 3. Mother-child interactions, family conflicts and maternal psychopathology. *Journal of Child Psychology and Psychiatry and Allied disciplines, 32*(2), 233-255.

44. Raberger, T., & Wimmer, H. (2003). On the automaticity / cerebellar deficit hypothesis of dyslexia: balancing and continuous rapid naming in dyslexic and ADHD children. *Neuropsychologia, 41*, 1493-1497.

45. Biederman, J., Faraone, S.V., Mick, E., Wozniak, J., Chen, L., Ouellette, C., et al. (1996). Attention-deficit hyperactivity disorder and juvenile mania: An overlooked comorbidity. *Journal of the American Academy of Child Adolescent Psychiatry, 35*, 997-1008.

46. Jain, U. (1999). Personality characteristics in Adult ADHD. *46th Annual Meeting of the American Academy of Child and Adolescent Psychiatry/ 19th Annual Meeting of the Canadian Academy of Child and Adolescent Psychiatry Association* October 19-24, Toronto, Canada.

47. Seligman, M.E. (1975). Helplessness: On depression, development, and death. A series of books in psychology. W.H. Freeman-Times Books, NY, NY. pp250.

48. Hooley, J. M. & Teasdale, J.D. (1989). Predictors of relapse in unipolar depressives: expressed emotion, marital distress, and perceived criticism. *Journal of Abnormal Psychology, 98*(3), 229-235.

49. Kessler, R.C., Adler, L., Barkley, R.A., Biederman, J., Conners, C.K., Demler, O., et al. (2006). The prevalence and correlates of adult ADHD in the United States: Results from the National Co-morbidity Survey Replication. *American Journal of Psychiatry, 163*, 716-723.

50. Fleming, J., & Levy, L. (2002). ADHD and Disordered Eating. In Quinn, P. & Nadeau, K. (Eds.), *Gender Issues and ADHD: Research, Diagnosis and Treatment,* Advantage Books, Silver Spring, MD. 411-426.

51. Cortese, S., Bernardina, B.D., & Mouren, M. (2007). Attention-deficit / hyperactivity disorder and binge eating. *Nutrition Reviews, 65*(9), 404-411.

52. Tannock, R. (2000). Attention deficit disorders with anxiety disorders. In T.E. Brown (Ed.), *Subtypes of attention deficit disorders in children, adolescents, and adults.* Washington, DC: American Psychiatric Press.

53. Pliszka, S. R., Carlson, C. L., & Swanson, J. M. (1999). ADHD with comorbid disorders: Clinical assessment and management. New York, NY: Guilford Press.

54. Law, S. F., & Schachar, R. J. (1999). Do typical clinical doses of methylphenidate cause tics in children treated for attention-deficit hyperactivity disorder? *Journal of the American Academy of Child and Adolescent Psyhciatry, 38*(8), 944-951.

55. Stolt, C. M. (1999). Moniz, lobotomy and the Nobel Prize 1949. *Sven Medical Tidskr, 3*(1), 249-270.

56. Angold, A., Costello, e.J., & erkanli, A. (1999). Comorbidity. *Journal of child Psychology and Psychiatry and Allied Disciplines, 40*(1), 57-87.

57. O'Malley KD, Nanson J. Clinical implications of a link between fetal alcohol spectrum disorder and attention deficit hyperactivity disorder. Can J Psychiatry-Revue Canadienne de Psychiatrie. 2002;47:349-354.

58. Rovet, J. F. & Hepworth, S. L. (2001). Dissociating attention deficits in children with ADHD and congenital hypothyroidism. *Journal of Child Psychology and Psychiatry, 42*(8), 1049-1056.

59. Vincent, A. (2009). My brain needs glasses: living with hyperactivity. Quebecor, Quebec, Canada.

60. Duncan, D.F. (1987). Lifetime prevalence of amotivational syndrome. *Psychology of Addictive Behaviors, 1*(2), 114-119.

61. Barkley, R.A., Edwards, G., Laneri, M., Fletcher, K., & Metevia, L. (2001). Executive functioning, temporal discounting, and sense of time in adolescents with attention deficit hyperactivity disorder (ADHD) and oppositional defiant disorder (ODD). *Journal of Abnormal Child Psychology, 29*(6), 541-556.

62. Ball, J. D., & Koloian, B. (1995). Sleep patterns among ADHD children. *Clinical Psychology Review, 15*(7), 681-691

63. Rybak, Y., McNeely, H.E., Mackenzie, B.E., Jain, U., Levitan, R. (2007). Seasonality and circadian preference in adult attention-deficit/hyperactivity disorder: clinical and neuropsychological correlates. *Comprehensive Psychiatry, 48*(6):562-71

64. Jain, U., Yoon, R., Shapiro, C. (2010). Update on Adult ADHD: Sleep Disorders in Adult ADHD *30ᵇ Annual Meeting of the Canadian Academy of Child and Adolescent Psychiatry*, September 25-28, Toronto, Canada

65. Drayer, D. C. & Horowitz, L. M. (1997). "When do opposites attract? Interpersonal complimentary versus similarity". *Journal of Personality and Social Psychology, 72*, 592–603.

About the Authors

RICK GREEN is an award-winning comedy writer, producer, director & actor. He's best known for co-creating and starring on *The Red Green Show, Prisoners of Gravity, History Bites* and *The Frantics: Four On The Floor*. In 2009 he and his wife Ava produced the award-winning documentary *ADD & Loving It?!*. This funny, fascinating program about fellow comedian Patrick McKenna became a hit on PBS, garnering acclaim & awards. It also spawned the groundbreaking website TotallyADD.com. Then that website spawned this book. And Rick spawned a couple of kids as well. Did we mention he has ADD? If we didn't, he will.

UMESH JAIN B.Sc., M.D., F.R.C.P.(C), D.A.B.P.N., Ph.D., M.Ed. is an internationally known psychiatrist specializing in ADHD. His hobby is earning degrees to impress his four children and his wife, a neonatal specialist, who all believe he is actually the gardener-janitor. He works in a University-based academic-teaching hospital in Toronto and founded the Canadian ADHD Resource Alliance (CADDRA) to help physicians, who specialize in ADHD. His parents believe he is a dermatologist and they are very proud of him. His one real gift has been translating complex medical information into simple understandable language. He's working to find another degree to prove it.